# SIMPLY SENSATIONAL

THE VICTOR CHANG

CARDIAC RESEARCH INSTITUTE

COOKBOOK

NUMBER THREE

Sally James

Author: Sally James

Managing editor: Philip Gore

Designer: Sharon McGrath

Recipe and copy editor: Loukie Werle

Consultant dietitian: Clare Rawcliffe

Recipe analysis: Rosemary Stanton

Marketing director: Stephen Balme

PHOTOGRAPHY AND STYLING

Photographer: Alan Benson

Food stylist: Michaela Le Compte

Food stylist's assistant: Rebecca Truda

Styling and food credits: The assistance of the following suppliers
is gratefully acknowledged: All Handmade; The Bay Tree;
Bisanna Tiles; Camargue; Funkis Swedish Forms; Made in Japan;
Papaya Studios; Planet Furniture; Plane Tree Farm; Spence & Lyda.

Packaged by

Media21 Publishing Pty Ltd

30 Bay Street, Double Bay, NSW 2028, Australia

Ph: (02) 9362 1800 Fax (02) 9362 9500

Email: m21@media21.com.au

Published by ACP Publishing Pty Limited

54 Park Street, Sydney, GPO Box 4088, Sydney, NSW 1028

Ph: (02) 9282 8000

© ACP Publishing Pty Limited 2002

ACN 053 273 546

© Recipes Sally James

Printed by Sino Publishing House Pty Ltd

Film separations by CJM Graphics Pty Ltd

National Library of Australia Cataloguing-in-Publication

James, Sally.

Simply Sensational : fresh, healthy and seasonal : Victor Chang Cardiac
Research Institute cookbook no.3.

Includes index.

ISBN 1 876624 95 7.

1. Low-fat diet - Recipes. 2. Heart- Diseases - Diet therapy - Recipes. I.
Victor Chang Cardia Research Institute. II. Title.

641.5638

Cover: Port Veal, Fig and Rocket Salad

Back cover: Fresh Pea Soup; Strawberry Tart

AUTHOR'S ACKNOWLEDGMENTS

Now on the third of this Victor Chang series I am more
grateful than ever for the 'dream team' who've drawn all
the elements together. The international awards for each
of the last books are proof of the magic of that team.

I would sincerely like to thank all those who have been so
important in helping 'Simply Sensational' come together.

To ACP for believing in the concept and publishing
the book. To the production team, Media 21, particularly
Stephen Balme, Philip Gore, Craig Osment and Loukie
Werle (editor 'extraordinaire') who shared the vision and
made the book what it is from beginning to end.
Their support, encouragement, patience and friendship
I will always appreciate.

To Professor Bob Graham, Jan Savage, Clare Rawcliffe
and all at the Victor Chang Cardiac Research Institute,
who have put their name behind the project with
excitement and enthusiasm. Their advice helped to keep
my recipes in boundaries that our bodies can be thankful
for without taking away what our palates delight in.
I am honoured once again to be able to contribute my
recipes to this very worthwhile cause and to
the memory of Victor Chang.

To the best 'vision team' an author could hope for –
the photographer, my friend Alan Benson, and Michaela
Le Compte, the stylist who makes my recipes look way
better than I ever dreamed. And to Rebecca Truda for
preparing the recipes for photography.

To Vallerga's Markets, my favourite gourmet supermarket
for quality produce and ingredients – my sincere thanks
for providing me with the freshest and best of the season
for creating the recipes and so many necessary
accompaniments. Special thanks to Ron, Randy, David,
Dylan for advice on the fish and meat, Erik and Kris on
seasonal produce, and Sue, Kathy, Scott, Gus, Mark, Ed
and Larry for their interest and friendly support.

To the many tasters who endured me testing recipes on
them without complaint – my wonderful new family.
including two very patient stepdaughters, Samantha and
Emily; my supportive in-laws. Steve and Christine Forrest;
Lori, Forrest, Aubrey and Alex Andrews; and the friends
who never said 'no' to a tasting at Sally and Stephen's,
Jan and Ken Austerman, Jane and John Brovelli,
Steve and Julie Raleigh, David Shipman and Vic Pinter;
and my own precious Mum and Dad.
All their opinions gave me something that allowed me to
learn and grow beyond my own boundaries.

But most of all to the man who supported, loved and
nurtured me through the whole process, enduring
months of meals in creation and kept me sane and
happier than ever through the whole process – my
husband and best friend, Stephen. For always believing
in me and encouraging me to explore new realms
without fear, my eternal thanks and love.

# SIMPLY SENSATIONAL

THE VICTOR CHANG

CARDIAC RESEARCH INSTITUTE

COOKBOOK

NUMBER THREE

## Sally James

PHOTOGRAPHY BY ALAN BENSON

STYLING BY MICHAELA LE COMPTE

# contents

# introduction

Presenting a whole new cornucopia of mouth-watering yet heart-healthy recipes, *Simply Sensational* promises to be a worthy successor to the Victor Chang Cardiac Research Institute's first two award winning cookbooks, *Simply Healthy*, which won the 1999 Versailles World Cookbook Fair, Best Health Cookbook Award, and *Fresh and Healthy*, which won in the Health and Special Diet Category of the International Association of Culinary Professionals Awards.

In *Simply Sensational*, Sally James has again teamed up with St Vincent's Hospital dietitian Clare Rawcliff, as well as Stephen Balme, Philip Gore and Craig Osment of Media 21 and the *Good Medicine* team at Australian Consolidated Press to create a new stable of healthy and delicious recipes – this time with a seasonal theme. Sally maintains that by buying produce that's in season, fresh and more flavoursome food can easily be prepared. Not only are her recipes sensational, they are of course designed to be good for your heart-health too! All are accompanied by a nutritional analysis to allow those with dietary restriction to simply and quickly ascertain their content of fat, sodium and kilojoules.

We hope those who are already Victor Chang Institute Cookbook junkies will feed their habit with *Simply Sensational*, while those who have yet to indulge, will give it a try.

Robert M. Graham, FAA, MD, FRACP, FACP
Executive Director
The Victor Chang Cardiac Research Institute

For questions, suggestions, changes and even criticisms, please access our website at www.victorchang.com.au

# the Victor Chang story

Victor Chang (Yam Him) was born in Shanghai in 1936 of Australian-born Chinese parents. He came to Australia in 1953 to complete his schooling at Christian Brothers College, Lewisham, and then moved on to medical training at Sydney University. Graduating in 1962, he became an intern and later a registrar in cardiothoracic surgery at St Vincent's Hospital. After completing additional training in England, and then at the prestigious Mayo Clinic in the US, he returned to St Vincent's Hospital in 1972 to join the elite St Vincent's cardiothoracic team that already included Henry Winsor and Mark Shanahan.

A pioneer of the modern era of heart transplantation, Victor Chang established the National Heart Transplant Unit at St Vincent's Hospital in 1984. During the 1980s, he became widely known as a man of vision, as a caring surgeon, as a researcher and as an ambassador for Australia and the people of South-East Asia. During this time, he nurtured a vision to establish an internationally recognised cardiac research centre at St Vincent's and, in 1990, he and others launched the "Heart of St Vincent's Appeal". With his tragic and untimely death in Sydney on 4 July 1991, efforts to realise Victor Chang's dream accelerated and resulted in generous donations from the federal government, Mr Kerry Packer, AC, and the Australian public. With these funds, St Vincent's Hospital established the Victor Chang Cardiac Research Institute, which was launched on 15 February 1994 by the Prime Minister of Australia, the Hon Paul Keating, with Kerry Packer as Patron and Professor Robert Graham as Director. On 27 February 1995 the Institute was incorporated as an independent research facility with the Hon Neville Wran, AC, QC, as Chairman, and, on 1 November 1996, Diana, Princess of Wales opened the Institute in its new premises.

The Institute is now a partner of the St Vincent's Campus and is affiliated with the University of New South Wales. In addition to conducting fundamental heart research, it is committed to providing excellence in cardiovascular research training and in facilitating the rapid application of research discoveries to patient care.

# healthy and sensational

We all know what we eat affects our health, but many of us are confused about what 'healthy eating' really means. The answer lies in enjoying a wide variety of nutritious foods with the ultimate goal of reducing heart disease risk factors – high blood cholesterol levels, high blood pressure, excess weight and high blood sugar levels if we have diabetes. Healthy food for the heart is healthy for all the family, and it can be simple and tasty.

## eat lots of fruit and vegetables

These foods are naturally low in fat, and any fat present is unsaturated – the good type for our heart. They are also low in salt, another bonus for heart health. Fruits and vegetables are high in fibre and contain antioxidants. Antioxidants are compounds that occur naturally in plant foods and have many functions that may include helping prevent heart disease, cancer and other degenerative diseases.

All fruits are healthy: fresh, canned or dried. All vegetables are great, too, either cooked or raw in salads. If you choose canned vegetables try the 'no added salt' version. Avocado, nuts and seeds are the only foods in this group that contain significant fat – but it's the healthy unsaturated type. In fact most experts encourage us to eat these foods more often because they contain other healthy nutrients that have been shown to improve heart health. It is best to choose unsalted nuts, and you will need to go easy if you are overweight.

Legumes include all the dried pea and bean family – baked beans, lentils, split peas, chickpeas, soy beans and many more – these vegetables are high in soluble fibre which is known to improve blood cholesterol levels and diabetes control. The soy bean is particularly popular among promoters of good health because of its phytoestrogen content. Phytoestrogens are natural plant sources of oestrogen and therefore may be related to improving heart and bone health, as well as helping alleviate some of the symptoms of menopause. Soy drinks, tofu, tempeh, soy breads and cereals are just some of the many soy foods now available.

Aim to eat at least two to three serves of fruit and at least four to five serves of vegetables each day.

### seven ways to eat more fruit and vegetables

- Include fresh fruit or fruit compote at breakfast, or add dried fruit to your cereal.
- Snack on fresh fruit, dried fruit or a fruit snack-pack during the day.
- Add lots of salad to your sandwich at lunch, or choose a side salad with your meal.
- Eat lots of vegetables or salad at your main meal and finish with a fruit-based dessert.
- Try one of the delicious legume recipes in this book.
- Sprinkle toasted nuts and seeds on your cereal, over a salad or incorporate in a recipe.
- Spread your bread with avocado or toss it through a salad.

# eat lots of breads and cereals

Like fruits and vegetables, most of these foods are also naturally low in saturated fat and high in fibre, particularly the wholegrain versions. They are also good sources of antioxidants and sometimes contain phytoestrogens. All types of breads, pastas, grains and most breakfast cereals are suitable. Aim to eat at least five or six serves from this group each day. Most breads and breakfast cereals are processed and therefore tend to have a high salt content. An alternative is to bake your own using one of the many bread-making machines now available and a mix without the salt. If this all sounds like too much trouble then remember the healthy qualities of bread probably outweigh its highish salt content, therefore you can continue to eat normal breads. Fortunately there are many breakfast cereals available in your supermarket which are low in salt.

## five ways to eat more bread and cereal

- Start your day with a fibre-rich cereal, such as rolled oats, natural muesli or wheat cereal.
- Have a bread-based lunch – preferably wholegrain bread with lean meat, chicken or fish and lots of salad.
- Try one of the many different varieties of grains – rice, barley, cracked wheat (tabouli), couscous, semolina, sago or tapioca.
- For a hot lunch choose pasta with a low fat sauce and a salad, or soup with lots of vegetables and pasta, or baked beans on toast.
- Vary your choice of bread – sliced, roll, pide, pita, focaccia, raisin, pumpkin – variety helps create more interest and stimulates the taste buds.

# choose lean meats and eat fish more often

There is no need to avoid meats and poultry, but go easy on your serve size. Lean meats and poultry without the skin are excellent sources of iron and zinc. Ideally the meat/poultry should only take up about a quarter to a fifth of your plate at the main meal – vegetables should take up the rest. Seafood is a great alternative.

The fats in fish are known to be heart-healthy, and most experts would recommend that you eat fish at least two to three times a week. Canned fish is also suitable. There are some wonderful fish recipes in this book.

Eggs are also very nutritious. You only need to limit them if you have a high blood cholesterol level, in which case two to three a week is quite acceptable.

# choose reduced-fat and low-fat dairy foods

Dairy foods are your best source of calcium – important for bone health.

The lower-fat versions are preferable since most of the fat in full-cream dairy foods is saturated. Aim to eat two to three serves of low fat dairy foods each day.

Remember the low-fat versions of dairy foods have just as much calcium in them, often more than their full-cream counterparts

# fats and oils

The types and amounts of fat/oil you use as a spread and in cooking are important. The better choices are those labelled polyunsaturated or monounsaturated. Grapeseed, safflower, and many margarines are polyunsaturated, while olive and canola are monounsaturated. These types of fats help lower blood cholesterol levels and have other heart-health benefits. If you are overweight be more conscious about the quantities you use – all types of fat are high in kilojoules/calories.

Recently, research has identified plant sterols to be particularly effective in lowering blood cholesterol levels. There are now margarines available that have been enriched with plant sterols. Although expensive, these spreads are effective in relatively small quantities (4–6 teaspoons daily). This food may be suited more specifically to those with a high blood cholesterol, rather than the whole family.

## keep active

Physical activity improves heart health and helps maintain a healthy body weight. Many people have difficulty keeping their weight within the healthy range. The wide availability of too many fatty foods that smell and taste good is too hard to resist for many of us. Furthermore, the growing trend of "automation" means that it becomes easier to move about less. Following the healthy eating principles on these pages and incorporating regular physical activity into our schedules are vital steps for good health. Simple things like using the stairs rather than the lift can add "movement" into your day with relative ease.

## indulgences

These are the foods we dream about but feel guilty when we do indulge. The news isn't all bad. Most lollies and sweets are not high in fat which means they can be eaten. But they are not high in nutritional value either and therefore recommended in moderation. Chocolate can be hard to resist, and although it is high in saturated fat, it does not seem to elevate blood cholesterol levels as expected. However, studies have unfortunately shown that the type of fat in chocolate is not good for heart-health for other reasons. Enjoy chocolate on special occasions. Unfortunately, most commercial cakes, pastries and biscuits contain a saturated fat called palm oil – the label commonly states 'vegetable oil'. Palm oil and coconut are the only vegetable foods high in saturated fat. Look for a low-fat biscuit/cake, or one where the label clearly states some sort of unsaturated fat is used. Alternatively bake your own, knowing you are using the right type of fat. Try one of the yummy recipes in this book.

Many snack foods and takeaway foods are high in saturated fat. Again, palm oil is commonly used, or sometimes beef tallow. These foods tend also to be high in salt. Rather than potato crisps, corn chips and fried takeaway foods, choose healthier options such as wholesome sandwiches, fruit, yoghurt or unsalted nuts.

Many people are eating out more often than ever before. Whenever you go to a restaurant, choose sensibly and don't be shy about asking for a healthier option.

## alcohol

If you drink alcohol, limit your intake. Small amounts of alcohol can improve heart health by increasing the levels of HDL cholesterol, ie, the 'good' type of cholesterol in your blood. Red wine seems to have additional benefits, possibly because it contains more antioxidants. However, for those who dislike red wine there are plenty of antioxidants in fruit and vegetables. Tea is also a good source of antioxidants.

You only need small amounts of alcohol to achieve these benefits. One or two standard alcoholic drinks a day (ie, 1-2 small glasses of wine) are sufficient. Drinking too much alcohol can lead to high blood pressure, diabetes, liver problems, heart failure, an increased risk of certain types of cancer, and can contribute to being overweight.

## salt

Try to choose low-salt foods and use salt sparingly. Eating too much salt can contribute to high blood pressure (hypertension) in some people. Most Australians eat too much salt and the majority comes from processed foods.

## in conclusion

Healthy-heart eating means variety and moderation. Go easy on fats, especially saturated fats, and also salt. Eat lots of fruit, vegetables, wholegrain breads and cereals. Balance your food intake with physical activity. Don't be too restrictive, enjoy.

– Clare Rawcliffe

# starters

# Chicken and Asparagus Rolls

**Makes 12 pastries**
345 kilojoules/83 calories per roll; **2.5g** total fat; **0.5g** saturated fat; **75mg** sodium

**Balsamic Glaze**
½ cup balsamic vinegar
1 teaspoon brown sugar
½ teaspoon salt reduced soy sauce

**Pastries**
3 chicken breast fillets, about 150g each
12 spears asparagus
6 sheets filo pastry
olive oil for brushing
1 tablespoon sesame seeds
24 basil leaves
pepper to taste

Preheat oven to 190°C.
Place ingredients for glaze in a saucepan and bring to the boil, reduce heat and simmer until mixture thickens to a light syrup, about 10-15 minutes. Allow to cool.
Remove any fat, skin and sinew from chicken and pound between sheets of plastic or baking paper with a mallet or rolling pin to about 1cm thickness. Cut each piece into 4 strips. Trim woody ends from asparagus.
Lay 2 sheets of filo pastry on a clean dry surface. Cut filo into 4 strips, fold each strip in half lengthwise. Brush each strip with olive oil, sprinkle with sesame seeds, and season to taste with pepper. Place a chicken strip on one end of pastry and brush with a little glaze. Place 2 basil leaves on the chicken followed by an asparagus spear. Roll up allowing pastry to work in a spiral to cover most of asparagus. Place, seam side down, on a lined or lightly oiled baking tray.
Bake for 15-20 minutes or until chicken is cooked through and pastry is crisp and brown.
Serve drizzled with remaining glaze.

Asparagus is a harbinger of spring, especially the new arrivals with plump, moist stems. Pick young spears that are thick, bright and crisp and snap off any woody stem.

# Low Salt Stock

2kg bones, choose from veal, beef, chicken carcasses, or use chicken wings
2 stalks celery, roughly chopped
1 large carrot, halved
1 onion, halved
1 whole garlic bulb, halved
handful parsley sprigs
about 12 peppercorns
splash white wine (helps to bring out the gelatine in the bones)

Combine all ingredients in a stockpot and cover generously with cold water. Bring to a boil, skim, and then simmer over very low heat for 4-6 hours. Drain, discarding solids, and pour into a large bowl. Refrigerate overnight.
Next day, remove any solidified fat from the surface. Freeze the stock in separate containers.

# Chilled Radish and Pear Soup

Serves 4

365 kilojoules/80 calories per serve; 3.5g total fat; 1g saturated fat; 60mg sodium

2 teaspoons olive oil
$^1/_4$ cup chopped leek
$^1/_4$ cup chopped celery
1 bunch young radish, about 8-10 heads, chopped
1 pear, chopped (for great colour use red pears)
$^1/_2$ cup low salt vegetable stock
1 cup low fat milk
1 tablespoon red wine vinegar
2 tablespoons low fat yoghurt or soft goat cheese,
    such as chevre
chopped dill leaves, to serve

Heat the oil over medium low heat in a large saucepan and cook the leek and celery for 2 minutes or until starting to soften. Add the radish and pear and cook, stirring for 1 minute. Pour in the stock, cover and simmer for 8-10 minutes or until pear is tender. Transfer to a blender or use an immersion blender and puree with the milk, vinegar and yoghurt or cheese.
Chill and serve topped with some chopped dill.

# Fresh Pea Soup

Serves 2

580 kilojoules/139 calories per serve; 1.5g total fat; 0.5g saturated fat; 55mg sodium

$^1/_2$ cup low salt vegetable broth
300g (about 2 cups) fresh or frozen peas
1-2 sprigs mint
$^1/_3$ cup low fat milk
1 tablespoon red wine vinegar
1 tablespoon medium dry sherry, optional
2 tablespoons low fat natural yoghurt
freshly ground pepper

Bring the stock to the boil, add the peas with half a mint sprig and simmer for 4-5 minutes or until tender. Drain, reserving liquid, and transfer to a blender.
Add a few fresh mint leaves, the milk, vinegar and sherry, and puree, adding a little of the reserved liquid if necessary to make a thick soup. Return to saucepan and reheat.
Serve the hot soup with a spoonful of yoghurt and a pepper grinder on the side.

Most people may opt to use frozen peas, which still makes a great soup, but for once, try it with some fresh plump spring peas, just to experience that garden freshness and texture.

# Gazpacho Gelees with Avocado Creme

**Serves 6**
**305** kilojoules/**72** calories per serve; **3g** total fat; **0.5g** saturated fat; **90mg** sodium

500ml salt reduced tomato juice or V8 juice
10g sachet gelatine
1 tablespoon vodka, optional
few drops tabasco sauce, optional
a squeeze of lemon juice
2 tablespoons chopped parsley
1 roma tomato, seeded and diced
1 lebanese cucumber, seeded and diced
freshly ground pepper to taste
4-6 x 10cm pieces celery

**Avocado Creme**
$^1/_2$ avocado
1 tablespoon lemon juice
2 tablespoons low fat plain yoghurt

Sprinkle the gelatine over 150ml of the juice in a small saucepan and stir over a low heat until dissolved. Add to the remaining ingredients, except the celery, in a large jug.
Pour into glasses or small bowls and place a celery stick in each one. Refrigerate until set.
To make avocado creme, mash the avocado and mix with the juice and yoghurt to a smooth paste. Just before serving top each glass with a spoon of the avocado creme.

I often make this in martini glasses for effect, with a celery stick propped up, as in a bloody mary.

# Smoked Salmon, Cucumber and Cheese Parcels

**Makes 12 parcels**

**170** kilojoules/**41** calories per serve; **2g** total fat; **1g** saturated fat; **310mg** sodium

- ⅓ cup grated lebanese or telegraph cucumber
- 2 tablespoons goat's cheese, such as chevre
- ¼ cup cottage cheese
- 1 tablespoon fresh dill leaves or mint
- 1 teaspoon lemon juice
- 12 small slices smoked salmon
- 12 long chives

Mash together the cucumber, cheeses, dill and lemon. Lay smoked salmon on a clean surface and place a heaped teaspoon of the cheese near one end of each slice. Wrap salmon around filling like a square parcel and secure with a chive. These make a great appetiser with crackers and champagne or a cocktail nibble. Try with the lavash recipe on page 18.

# Zucchini Basil Soup with Lemon Crostini

**Serves 4**

**905** kilojoules/**216** calories per serve; **11g** total fat; **2g** saturated fat; **170mg** sodium

- 1 tablespoon olive oil
- ½ cup sliced leek
- 1 stalk celery, chopped
- 4 zucchini, about 400g, chopped
- 1 cup low salt chicken stock (see page 12) or white wine
- 5-6 leaves fresh basil
- 1 tablespoon lemon juice
- 100ml buttermilk
- freshly ground pepper to taste

**Lemon Crostini**
- 1 tablespoon olive oil
- 1 tablespoon lemon juice, plus 2 teaspoons lemon zest
- 4 slices Italian bread or ciabatta

Heat the oil in a large saucepan and saute the leek and celery for 1-2 minutes or until soft. Add the zucchini and stock, cover and bring to the boil. Reduce heat and simmer for 10-15 minutes or until zucchini is soft. Place in a blender with the basil, lemon juice and buttermilk and puree until smooth. Season and return to saucepan to reheat.

While the soup is cooking, mix together the oil, lemon juice and zest and brush over one side of the bread. Season to taste with pepper if desired.

Bake in a hot oven for 3-5 minutes or until golden brown. Serve with the soup.

# Pear, Parmesan and Prosciutto Wraps

**Makes 9**
**185** kilojoules/**44** calories per serve; **1.5g** total fat; **1g** saturated fat; **175mg** sodium

1/4 cup shredded parmesan cheese
1/4 cup fine breadcrumbs
2-3 leaves fresh basil, finely shredded
lemon juice
5 slices lean prosciutto, cut in half lengthwise
2 pears, cut into 6 slices each (you'll need only 9 slices)

Preheat oven to 190°C. Line an oven tray with baking paper. Combine the cheese, breadcrumbs and basil in a bowl and mix well. Spoon 12 mounds on the baking paper and flatten with a spatula. Bake for 8-10 minutes or until golden brown and set. (You can also do this in a non-stick pan but take care not to burn them). Remove from oven and allow to cool slightly before lifting off paper with a metal spatula and cooling completely on a wire rack.
Wrap prosciutto around a slice of pear and serve immediately on a parmesan crisp. These are great served with lavash or rye crispbread and a sharp semillon.

For this recipe, it's better to get the fresh parmesan shredded in strands rather than a finely grated dried version.

# Roasted Wild Mushroom Soup

**Serves 2**

**365** kilojoules/**87** calories per serve; **1.5g** total fat; **0.5g** saturated fat; **55mg** sodium

> 250g mixed mushrooms, cleaned, such as oyster, shitake, portabella, swiss brown, button
> 3-4 leaves fresh basil
> $^1/_4$ cup white wine
> $^1/_2$ cup low fat milk
> freshly ground pepper to taste

Preheat oven to 175°C.

Lay mushrooms, stem side up, on an oven tray lined with baking paper. Make sure baking paper goes over the edges of the tray so you can catch the liquid. Roast for 10-15 minutes or until mushrooms are soft and have started to loose their juices. Transfer mushrooms with their juice to a food processor, reserving two whole mushrooms for the top. Add the basil, wine, milk and pepper and process to a puree, adding a little more milk if too thick. Pour into a saucepan and heat to a simmer. Serve topped with the reserved whole mushrooms.

# Red Wine and Olive Oil Crackers

**Makes about 50 crackers**

**535** kilojoules/**128** calories per serve; **6.5g** total fat; **1g** saturated fat; **5mg** sodium

> 1 cup plain flour
> $^1/_2$ cup wholemeal flour or rolled oats
> $^1/_4$ cup red wine (the crackers will be tastier with a rich bold wine)
> $^1/_4$ cup olive oil
> $^1/_4$ cup buttermilk

Sift the flours together into a large bowl. Make a well in the centre. Whisk the wine, oil and buttermilk together and pour into the well. Mix quickly and lightly with a knife until mixture comes together. Knead slightly on a floured surface to form a smooth dough. Cover with plastic wrap and refrigerate for $^1/_2$ hour. Preheat oven to 180°C.

Roll out dough on a sheet of baking paper the same size as the oven tray to about a thickness of $^1/_2$ cm. At this stage you could incorporate a flavour by brushing with egg white or milk and sprinkling with herbs, pepper, sesame seeds, etc. I like just a dusting of pepper-seasoned flour for a rustic look. With a sharp knife, mark dough into crackers, cutting right through.

Bake for 15-20 minutes or until golden brown and crisp. Transfer baking paper to a wire rack to cool, before breaking into crackers and storing in a sealed container.

These will keep for up to a month.

These are my favourite crackers for serving in front of a log fire with some sliced autumn pear, olives and a glass of rich red.

# One Dough,
# Three Recipes

**Yeasted Dough**

1 sachet (2$^1/4$ teaspoons) dried yeast

1 cup warm water

3$^1/4$ cups flour

3 cups warm water, extra

pinch sea salt, optional

Mix the yeast with the warm water and dissolve completely. Add $^1/2$ cup of the flour and stir well. Cover loosely and leave in a warm place for 30 minutes or until the dough becomes bubbly and light, like a sponge.

Transfer to a mixer fitted with a dough hook, add the extra water, flour and salt and process for 3-4 minutes or until dough leaves sides of bowl and springs back when pressed. Alternatively, knead on a floured surface for 10 minutes. Place the dough in a lightly oiled bowl and turn so the dough is totally coated with oil. Cover with a damp cloth and allow to rise in a warm place for 1$^1/2$-2 hours or until doubled in bulk. Punch dough down and allow to rise again for 20-30 minutes. I sometimes like to leave the mixture in the fridge overnight for a wonderful chewy texture and crisp crust. You can also freeze it at this stage for future use. The dough is now ready for the following recipes.

There's nothing quite like the smell and warmth of freshly made bread on a cool winter's day. This dough makes enough for a few different recipes, but if you make one large batch then you can have piroshki for lunch, foccacia with dinner and lavash for the next few weeks. Or, turn to the salad section and discover the wonderful hot bread, cold salad piadine. This also makes a great base for pizzas: be adventurous and try varieties such as pesto and mushroom, mozzarella and rocket, shredded chicken and peanut sauce, lamb and minted ricotta.

# Focaccia

**Makes 4 x 18cm rounds, or 2 long focaccias 25cm x 12cm**
**2090** kilojoules/**499** calories per round; **11g** total fat;
**1.5g** saturated fat; **60mg** sodium

1 quantity yeasted dough (see left)

2 tablespoons extra virgin olive oil

1 tablespoon fresh rosemary leaves

**Topping Ideas**

rocket leaves, lemon strips, grilled prosciutto, capers

thinly sliced tomato, red onion, basil

sliced capsicum, fennel and oregano

fresh shaved artichoke, fennel and thyme

grated fresh horseradish, thinly sliced potato, ricotta and
    parsley

freshly ground black pepper, radicchio

Preheat oven to 230°C.

Shape dough into a round or two large rectangles. With fingertips, make shallow indentations in top of dough. Brush with olive oil, so it slides into holes, and scatter with rosemary. Top with desired toppings and bake for 12-15 minutes or until golden brown and hollow sounding when tapped. Serve hot or cold.

This is a slight twist on traditional focaccia with the oil on top of the bread and not in the mix. It can be made plain or using any of your favourite toppings.

# Caprese Piroshki

**Makes about 24**

**1300** kilojoules/**310** calories per serve of 3 piroshki; **9.5g** total fat; **3g** saturated fat; **160mg** sodium

¹/₂ cup pitted olives
¹/₂ teaspoon dijon mustard
1-2 tablespoons lemon juice
1 quantity yeasted dough (see page 24
12 basil leaves, halved
6 medium bocconcini, each cut into 4 slices
24 cherry tomatoes
2 tablespoons olive oil
2 tablespoons shredded parmesan cheese

Preheat oven to 220°C.
Soak the olives in water for 30 minutes to remove excess salt. Rinse, drain and pat dry with paper towels. In a food processor, combine olives with the mustard and enough lemon juice to make a paste. Set aside.
Roll out the dough on a lightly floured surface to about ¹/₂cm thickness. Cut into rounds using a 9-10cm cookie or scone cutter. Spread the centre of each round with a small amount of the olive paste. Lay a piece of basil over the paste, followed by the bocconcini, then top with a tomato. Make sure none of the ingredients come near the edges of the dough. Brush edges lightly with water and bring up over the filling to make a ball. Press edges together to seal well.
Brush the smooth side of each ball with oil and dip in parmesan then transfer to non-stick or lined baking trays. Bake for 15-20 minutes or until golden brown. Serve hot or cold.

# Lavash with Avocado Yoghurt Cheese

**Makes about 30 lavash, and 2 cups Avocado Yoghurt Cheese**

**370** kilojoules/**89** calories per lavash; **3g** total fat; **0.5g** saturated fat; **20mg** sodium

**Lavash**
¹/₂ quantity yeasted dough (see page 24)
1-2 tablespoons olive oil for brushing
**Topping Ideas**
sesame seeds, chopped pistacchio, coriander powder
mustard seeds, pepper and red pepper flakes
poppy seeds, dried thyme and oregano
ground pepper, diced almonds and hazelnuts
chopped macadamias and ginger

Preheat oven to 200°C.
Roll out dough to about 2-3mm thickness. If you have a pasta machine, this will make the thinnest dough. Otherwise roll out between sheets of baking paper as thinly as possible, or cut off small pieces of dough and roll individual lavash.
Carefully transfer to non-stick or lightly oiled baking sheets. It doesn't matter if it tears a little – this adds to the character. Brushlightly with oil and sprinkle over garnishes. Cover with baking paper and roll over top with a rolling pin to press in toppings. Allow to rest for 10-15 minutes.
With a sharp knife, mark into triangles or slices, about 12 x 4cm-5cm or as desired. Bake for 2-3 minutes, then rotate pans and bake until browned and crisp, about 5-6 minutes in total. Keep an eye on them as they brown quickly.
Allow to cool on wire racks, then break into shapes and store in an airtight container for up to 2-3 weeks.

**Avocado Yoghurt Cheese**
2 cups low fat plain yoghurt (for an interesting flavour, try with goat's or sheep's milk yoghurt)
freshly ground black pepper
1 tablespoon lemon zest
1 large avocado, mashed (about ¹/₂ cup)
2 teaspoons lemon juice
¹/₂ teaspoon chilli sauce, or to taste
¹/₄ cup finely chopped fresh coriander

Combine the yoghurt and pepper. Line a colander or strainer with a double thickness of muslin or cheesecloth and spoon in the yoghurt. Place over a large bowl and cover with plastic wrap. Allow to drain overnight, pressing out any excess liquid when finished. Combine with remaining ingredients and mix well.

# seafood

# Fish in Filo with Raspberry Sauce

**Serves 4**

**1545** kilojoules/**369** calories per serve; **12g** total fat; **3g** saturated fat; **355mg** sodium

**Raspberry Sauce**

$1/2$ cup fresh or frozen, defrosted, raspberries

2 tablespoons red wine

1 tablespoon brown sugar

**Fish**

4 x 150g firm white boneless fish fillets such as blue eye, gemfish, flake or mahi mahi

freshly ground pepper

2 tablespoons lemon zest

8 sheets filo pastry

2 tablespoons olive oil

$1/2$ small fennel bulb, finely sliced

1 small bunch baby rocket

mixed herbs

Preheat oven to 200°C.

Puree the sauce ingredients in a food processor until smooth. Set aside. Remove skin from fish fillets and season to taste with pepper and lemon zest.

Lay 2 sheets of filo pastry on a clean dry surface. Brush lightly with olive oil. Lay a quarter of the fennel on one end, leaving 2-3cm at sides for folding in. Top with a quarter of the rocket and lay on a fish fillet. Fold in the ends and roll up the fish in the pastry, brushing top lightly with oil. Lay on a non-stick or baking paper lined oven tray. Repeat with remaining pastry, vegetables and fish.

Bake for 10-12 minutes or until pastry is golden brown. If the fillets are thick, you may need a few minutes longer.

Fish should just flake when pressed with a knife.

Serve with the raspberry sauce.

With spring, the warmer weather brings promise of so much wonderful fruit such as berries. I've chosen raspberries to match this fish in filo, but this sauce is also great with salmon, chicken or even over ice cream.

# Stir-fry Snap Peas and Scallops

Serves 4

420 kilojoules/**100** calories per serve; **1g** total fat; **0.5g** saturated fat; **515mg** sodium

- 1 tablespoon salt reduced soy sauce
- 1 tablespoon oyster sauce
- 2 tablespoons mirin or sherry
- 2 teaspoons grated fresh ginger
- 24 scallops without roe
- 1 tablespoon olive oil
- 400g sugar snap peas, trimmed
- cooked rice, to serve

Combine the sauces, mirin and ginger and pour over the scallops. Cover and marinate for 1 hour. Drain and reserve marinade. Heat half the oil in a wok or large non-stick pan and stir-fry the peas for 1 minute or until tender crisp. Remove from pan and set aside.

Heat the remaining oil and stir-fry the scallops for 1-2 minutes or until just cooked and browned on both sides. Add the peas and reserved marinade and stir-fry until heated through.

Serve in bowls with some rice or noodles on the side.

# Seafood Lettuce Parcels with Wasabi Cucumber Yoghurt

Serves 4

590 kilojoules/**141** calories per serve; **2g** total fat; **1g** saturated fat; **295mg** sodium

**Wasabi Cucumber Yoghurt**
- $1/4$ cup low fat plain yoghurt
- $1/2$ teaspoon wasabi paste, or to taste
- 1 tablespoon lime juice
- $1/2$ lebanese cucumber, grated

**Parcels**
- 500g mixed raw seafood – try green prawns, scallops, diced ocean trout and blue eye
- 1 tablespoon chopped fresh lemongrass
- 1 tablespoon grated fresh ginger
- juice and grated zest of 1 lime
- $1/4$ cup fresh chopped coriander
- 2 tablespoons rice wine or dry white wine
- 2 tablespoons light coconut milk
- 1 teaspoon sweet chilli sauce or green curry paste, or to taste
- 1 shallot, chopped
- 8 large butter lettuce leaves (or iceberg), centre hard stalk removed

Preheat oven to 200°C.

Combine the Wasabi Cucumber Yoghurt ingredients and set aside. Place all the seafood in a large bowl.

In a mortar and pestle or grinder, crush the lemongrass, ginger and lime zest together. Mix with the juice, coriander, rice wine, coconut milk and chilli and toss this through the seafood.

Cut 4 sheets of baking paper, about 25cm long.

If you are using a very crisp iceberg leaf you may need to blanch for 20-30 seconds to soften the leaf. Otherwise, just place fresh lettuce leaf on each sheet and spoon a quarter of the seafood mixture on the centre of each leaf, making sure to incorporate the seasonings and liquid evenly. Wrap the lettuce tightly around the seafood. Bring the long edges of the paper together and fold over like a sandwich, securing the parcels well. Twist the ends to seal. Place parcels on a baking tray and bake for 10-15 minutes. Open one of the parcels to test.

The prawns should be opaque and the fish just start to flake when pressed with a fork. Take care not to overcook.

Remove lettuce parcels from paper and serve with the yoghurt. Make sure to tip any remaining juices in the paper over the fish.

# Vietnamese-style Marinated Prawn Baguettes

**Makes 4**

1545 kilojoules/369 calories per serve; 5g total fat;
1g saturated fat; 880mg sodium

**Marinade**

2 teaspoons salt reduced soy sauce

1 teaspoon sugar

1 tablespoon rice wine vinegar (or wine vinegar)

16-20 raw king prawns, peeled and deveined

**Spread**

2 teaspoons Asian chilli paste or sweet chilli sauce

2 tablespoons plain yoghurt or buttermilk

2 teaspoons marmalade, optional

1 teaspoon powdered ginger

pinch of cinnamon

pinch of Chinese five spice or allspice

1 teaspoon olive or peanut oil

1 shallot, chopped

**To serve**

4 pieces baguette, about 20cm each

mixed leaves

chopped basil and/or mint

1 cup sliced cucumber

Combine the marinade ingredients and toss through the prawns.
Marinate in the refrigerator for 30 minutes.
Combine the spread ingredients and set aside.
In a non-stick pan, combine the ginger, cinnamon, spice
and oil and cook over medium heat until aromatic, about
20-30 seconds. Add the shallots and prawn mixture and stir over
medium heat until prawns are cooked.
Spread baguettes with the chilli mixture, top with the mixed
leaves, cucumber, prawns and basil.
Close baguette and eat while warm. You could also chill
the cooked prawns and serve this as a cold sandwich.

I have often made this dish with sliced white
fish, chicken breast and ground pork –
even tofu would work well, so don't feel
bound to use prawns.

# Rare Seared Tuna Salad

**Serves 4 as a light meal**
**1650** kilojoules/**395** calories per serve; **23g** total fat; **4g** saturated fat; **175mg** sodium

500g fillet sashimi grade tuna
2 tablespoons black sesame seeds (or white)
1 tablespoon cracked pepper
2 teaspoons extra virgin olive oil

**Wasabi Dressing**
2 tablespoons extra virgin olive oil
2 tablespoons lemon juice
$1/2$ teaspoon wasabi powder or paste, or to taste
few drops truffle oil, optional

**Ginger Yoghurt**
$1/4$ cup low fat plain yoghurt
2 teaspoons grated fresh, or bottled ginger

**Salad**
6 thick plump spears asparagus, finely sliced diagonally
10cm piece telegraph or lebanese cucumber, cut into matchsticks
2 witlof, finely sliced
$1/2$ cup finely sliced fennel
1 mango, cut into matchsticks
2 tablespoons rice wine vinegar
1 teaspoon salt reduced soy sauce

Coat the fish in sesame seeds and pepper, pressing in well. Heat the oil in a non-stick pan and sear fish for 30 seconds each side. The centre should not be cooked. Transfer to a plate, cover loosely and chill in the refrigerator.

Whisk together the wasabi dressing ingredients and stir the yoghurt and ginger together. Set aside.

Toss all the salad ingredients in a bowl and arrange in the centre of plates or one large platter. If desired, drizzle with a few drops of the truffle oil.

Slice the fish as thinly as possible and arrange around the outside of the salad. Drizzle with the wasabi dressing. Spoon the yoghurt in mounds around the salad or serve on the side.

Before buying the fish for this salad, ask your fishmonger if it is suitable to eat raw, as the fish is only very lightly cooked.

# Grape-glazed Tuna with Lemon Risoni

**Serves 4**
**2820** kilojoules/**673** calories per serve; **7g** total fat; **1g** saturated fat; **90mg** sodium

500g risoni pasta (orzo)
juice and zest of $\frac{1}{2}$ lemon
3 teaspoons extra virgin olive oil
4 tuna fillets, about 130-150g each
freshly ground pepper

**Glaze**

1 teaspoon olive oil
1 green onion, white part only, chopped
1 cup red wine (try pinot or shiraz)
$\frac{1}{2}$ cup low salt chicken stock (see page 12)
100g red grapes

To make the glaze, heat the olive oil in a small saucepan, add the green onion and cook until soft.
Pour in the red wine and stock and simmer for 10-15 minutes or until reduced by about half. Add the grapes, mashing slightly to release their juices and cook until mixture thickens to a syrup. Puree, strain and set aside.
Cook risoni according to directions on packet, drain and toss through the lemon and 1 teaspoon of the oil. Keep warm.
Heat the remaining oil in a non-stick pan and sear the tuna over high heat for 1-2 minutes each side – it should still be red inside for the most tender, moist and flavoursome result. Serve on the risoni and spoon over the glaze either warm or cold.

# Crab, Avocado and Grapefruit Salad with Beet Puree

**Serves 2 as a meal with bread**
**1640** kilojoules/**391** calories per serve; **27g** total fat; **5g** saturated fat; **785mg** sodium

**Red Beet Puree**

2 beetroots, scrubbed
2 tablespoons low fat plain yoghurt
1 tablespoon lemon juice or orange juice
freshly ground pepper to taste

**Crab Salad**

1 tablespoon extra virgin olive oil or lemon oil
1 tablespoon lemon juice
2 teaspoons horseradish mustard
2 tablespoons fresh dill or 2 teaspoon dried dill leaves
1 avocado, sliced
1 pink grapefruit, segmented and pith removed
1 bunch fresh watercress, rocket or frisee
200g can chunk crabmeat, drained, or get fresh if you can

Preheat oven to 190-200°C.
Wrap the beets separately in foil and bake for 30-40 minutes or until tender. Cool and peel. Combine the beets with the yoghurt, lemon and pepper in a food processor and whiz until smooth. Whisk the oil, juice, mustard and dill for the salad together. Mix the avocado, grapefruit and crab in a bowl and toss gently with the dressing.
To serve, arrange the salad on a plate and arrange the crab on top. Serve with the beetroot puree separately. Top with extra chopped dill if desired.
Serve with crusty bread and extra virgin olive oil.

Graham Kerr once told me the story of
an Indian chief he met in North America who
was an avid salmon fisherman. When Graham
asked what he liked best to do with
the salmon, his reply was to open a tin of
white beans, pour them into a large ovenproof
dish with some summer savory, top with
a side of salmon and rub with cut garlic.
Since that time, it's become one of my most
popular, easy and favourite dishes when
having friends over. I actually prefer it
drizzled with a little diluted truffle oil and
finished off under a hot grill to give the fish
a crisp crust – the choice is yours.

For a lower salt alternative, soak dried
cannellini beans overnight, or quick-soak.
To quick-soak, cover the beans in a pan
with 5cm water and bring to a boil.
Boil 1-2 minutes, cover with a lid and set
aside for 60 minutes.

# Side of Salmon on White Beans

**Serves 6**
**With canned beans: 1180** kilojoules/**281** calories per serve;
**8g** total fat; **1.5g** saturated fat; **410mg** sodium
**With dried beans: 1230** kilojoules/**294** calories per serve;
**8g** total fat; **1.5g** saturated fat; **75mg** sodium

1 side of salmon, deboned (800g-1kg)
2 x 400g cans salt reduced white or cannellini beans or
   250g dried cannellini beans (see box)
1/2 cup chopped fresh summer savory or chervil
1 clove garlic or few drops truffle oil in 1 tablespoon olive oil
freshly ground pepper

Preheat oven to 190°C.
Remove the skin from the salmon. If you're deboning it yourself,
find the bones by pressing the flesh with your fingers and
remove them one by one with tweezers.
If using dried beans, drain and place in a pan, covered with fresh
water. Bring slowly to a boil, then simmer gently for
40-60 minutes, or until the beans are tender. Drain, reserving
about 1/4 cup of the cooking water. Spread the beans in a large
ovenproof dish, pour over the reserved cooking water. For
canned beans, drain most of the liquid from the beans and
spread over the base of a large ovenproof dish.
Sprinkle beans with the summer savory. Lay the salmon over
the beans and rub the flesh with cut garlic or drizzle with the oil.
Season to taste with pepper if desired.
Bake for 10 minutes or until flesh just starts to flake but is still
pink inside. If you like a crisp crust, pop under a hot grill for
1 minute and serve at the table straight away with some
steamed green beans or a crisp salad and bread.

# Salmon with Pilau

Serves 4

**1865** kilojoules/**445** calories per serve; **13g** total fat;
**2.5g** saturated fat; **130mg** sodium

4 fillets salmon, skin and bones removed
freshly ground pepper

**Barley Pilau**

2 teaspoons olive oil, plus 1 tablespoon extra, for the salmon
$^1/_2$ red onion, finely diced
1 cup (250g) pearl barley
1$^1/_2$ cups low salt vegetable or chicken stock (see page 12)
1 cup white wine
few handfuls shredded radicchio, optional
1 small fennel bulb, cut in $^1/_2$cm dice
juice and zest of 1 lemon
$^1/_4$ cup small black olives, preferably Ligurian

To make the pilau, heat the oil in a large saucepan and cook
the onion for 1-2 minutes or until starting to soften and brown.
Add the barley, and cook, stirring for 1 minute. Add the stock,
wine and radicchio and bring to the boil. Reduce heat, cover and
simmer, stirring occasionally, for 30-40 minutes, or until barley is
tender and liquid is absorbed. Add a little water if mixture
becomes too dry. Fold in the fennel, lemon juice and zest and
olives and remove from heat.
Brush the salmon fillets with oil and season with pepper. Heat
a grill pan or frying pan and sear the salmon for 1-2 minutes on
each side or until cooked as preferred.

# Curried Scallops with Cauliflower Puree

Serves 4

**1080** kilojoules/**258** calories per serve; **12g** total fat; **2g** saturated
fat; **340mg** sodium

600g scallops, without roe
2 tablespoons extra virgin olive oil
2 teaspoons mild curry powder
$^3/_4$ teaspoon ground ginger
$^1/_2$ teaspoon brown sugar

**Cauliflower Puree**

500g cauliflower, chopped
1 potato, peeled and finely diced
$^1/_4$ cup low fat milk, or to taste
juice and zest of 1 lemon
1 tablespoon capers
$^1/_4$ cup fresh basil or mint leaves

Place the scallops in a plastic bag and add 1 tablespoon of
the oil. Toss gently to coat. Add the curry, ginger and sugar and
toss again so all the scallops are coated. Refrigerate until ready
to cook. Cook the cauliflower and potato in boiling water or
low salt vegetable stock until soft. Mash with an immersion
blender or potato masher with the milk and juice, adding
more milk, if needed, to create a smooth mash. Fold in
the capers and basil or mint and keep warm.
Heat a large non-stick pan and add the remaining oil. Add
the scallops and cook for 1-2 minutes on each side or
until just cooked, but still plump and firm. They should just
start to lose a bit of their juices.
Spoon hot puree on to plates and top with the scallops and pan
juices. Serve with a rocket, watercress and lemon zest salad.

# Braised Vegetables with Pan-fried Seafood

**Serves 4**

**1600** kilojoules/**383** calories per serve; **12g** total fat; **2g** saturated fat; **435mg** sodium

**For The Braise**

- 1 cup water
- 2 tablespoons sugar
- 3 leaves fresh sage, or $1/2$ teaspoon dried
- 1 small sprig each fresh rosemary and thyme
  (or 1 teaspoon dried leaves)
- 1 parsnip
- 1 turnip
- 1 carrot
- 250g piece pumpkin, about 1 cup diced
- 1 tablespoon extra virgin olive oil
- 1 cup shelled broadbeans
- few leaves oregano

**Potato Puree**

- 3 large white potatoes, peeled
- $1/4$-$1/2$ cup skim milk or buttermilk
- pepper to taste
- few drops truffle oil, optional (see note)

**Seafood**

- 1 tablespoon olive oil
- 300g peeled raw king prawns
- 300g scallops without roe

Boil the sugar and water until sugar is dissolved. Add the herbs and simmer for 5 minutes or until the syrup has taken on the flavours. Allow to cool.

Dice the parsnip, turnip, carrot and pumpkin (about 1cm) and lightly blanch till just tender crisp. Drain and pat dry with a paper towel. (These two steps can be done well in advance and the final dish assembled just before serving.)

Heat the oil in a non-stick frying pan and saute the diced vegetables for 3-4 minutes or until browned, add the broadbeans, syrup and oregano and simmer until broadbeans are cooked, about 5 minutes. Keep warm.

Meanwhile, boil, drain and puree the potatoes, adding enough milk to make a smooth and soft mash. Season to taste with the pepper and truffle oil, if using. Keep warm.

Heat the oil in a separate pan and, just before serving, pan-fry the prawns and scallops for 1-2 minutes on each side or until cooked through.

Place potato puree on plates, spoon over the braised vegetables with a little of the liquid and top with the seafood.

I always keep a small bottle of truffle oil on hand to add a lift to dishes.
It's expensive but you only need a drop or two for a lot of flavour – you can also dilute it with extra virgin olive oil to make it go further.

Other firm, mild white fish such as blue eye, flake, mahi mahi or halibut would work well with this dish.

# Swordfish with Braised Radicchio and Capers

**Serves 4**

**1325** kilojoules/**317** calories per serve; **14g** total fat; **3g** saturated fat; **280mg** sodium

1 large radicchio or witlof
2 teaspoons extra virgin olive oil
juice and zest of 2 oranges
$^1/_2$ cup wine, low salt vegetable stock or water
2 tablespoons Cointreau
2 tablespoons drained capers
4 swordfish fillets (about 150g each)

Cut the radicchio into quarters lengthwise. Heat half the oil in a non-stick pan and pan-fry the radicchio on both cut sides for 1-2 minutes, then pour in the juice and stock.
Simmer for 5-6 minutes or until radicchio is starting to soften. Remove radicchio from the pan and keep warm.
Stir the Cointreau into the pan and reduce the liquid for 5 minutes. Add the capers and keep warm.
In separate pan or grill, cook the fish in the remaining oil for 2-3 minutes each side or until cooked as desired. For the most moist and tender result, cook fish for the shortest possible time.
Serve fish with the radicchio and the caper sauce.

# Grilled Fish with Warm Beetroot Relish and Saffron Orange Rice

**Serves 4**

**1600** kilojoules/**382** calories per serve; **4g** total fat; **1g** saturated fat; **90mg** sodium

**Relish**
1 large or 2-3 baby beets, peeled and grated
  (about $^1/_2$ -$^3/_4$ cup)
$^1/_2$ cup red wine
$^1/_3$ tablespoon red wine vinegar
2 tablespoons brown sugar
2 tablespoons lemon or orange juice

**Rice**
1 cup basmati or long grain rice
few strands saffron
juice and zest of 1 navel orange
2 tablespoons chopped fresh coriander or basil

4 x 130-150g fillets firm fish (eg mahi mahi, blue eye, swordfish, ocean trout or salmon)

To make the relish, combine all the ingredients in a small saucepan on a medium heat, stirring until mixture boils. Reduce heat and keep warm until ready to serve.
Boil the rice with the saffron until al dente. Drain, toss through the orange juice, zest and coriander and keep warm.
Preheat a non-stick or grill pan and brush with oil. Sear the fish for 1-2 minutes on each side or until cooked as desired. When the flesh just starts to flake, remove from the heat, as it continues to cook on the plate and may become tough and dry.
Serve the fish over the rice with the relish.

# meat & poultry

# Meat Pie and Peas

**Serves 4**

**2845** kilojoules/**680** calories per serve; **28g** total fat; **6g** saturated fat; **480mg** sodium

**Pastry**

1 cup plain flour

1 cup self-raising flour

$1/4$ cup olive oil

$1/3$ cup skim milk

**Filling**

1 tablespoon olive oil

1 onion, diced

1 stick celery, chopped

1 carrot, chopped

500g lean minced beef

$1/2$ cup tomato juice or puree

$1/2$ cup strong black tea

1 cup beer (or low salt stock, but the beer makes a rich, sweet flavour – not beery at all)

**Peas**

2 cups fresh or frozen peas

1 sprig mint

To make pastry, sift flours into a large bowl. Whisk together the oil and milk and pour into the flours. Mix quickly and lightly with a knife until mixture comes together. Transfer to a well-floured surface and knead lightly to a smooth dough. Wrap in plastic and refrigerate 30 minutes.

Heat the oil in a large saucepan and cook the onion, celery and carrot for 2-3 minutes or until starting to brown. Add the mince and cook, stirring, until lightly browned. Pour in the liquids and cook, stirring occasionally, for 10 minutes or until liquid is mostly absorbed. Allow to cool to warm. You could also make this the day before and bake the pie(s) the next day.

Preheat oven to 180°C.

Fill 2 x 1$1/2$ cup capacity pie dishes with the meat mixture (there may be some left over). Thinly roll out 2 circles of the dough to cover pies. Lay on top, trim, and pinch edges to seal. Make a few slashes on top with a sharp knife and bake for 20-25 minutes or until well browned.

Just before pie(s) are cooked, steam or microwave peas with mint until just tender. Mash slightly and keep warm. Season to taste with pepper.

A very fond childhood memory for me is of spring peas fresh from the garden with a meat pie – which I'd lift the lid off and fill with the peas – being a chronic 'food player'. Here's a slightly healthier version than the one I had back then.

# Pork with Plum Relish

**Serves 4**

**1070** kilojoules/**256** calories per serve; **7.5g** total fat;
**1.5g** saturated fat; **115mg** sodium

**Relish**

> ½ red onion, diced
> 2 teaspoons olive oil
> 1 tablespoon brown sugar
> 1 cup diced plums (3-4 of any type of plum)
> 1 tablespoon balsamic or red wine vinegar
> 1 tablespoon lemon juice
> ¼ cup white wine
> dash soy sauce, optional
>
> 4 pork fillets (about 600g total)
> olive oil
> lemon juice or balsamic vinegar
> mixed lettuce

To make the relish, sweat the onion in the oil over a medium heat until soft. Add the sugar and plums and cook, stirring for 2-3 minutes then add remaining ingredients. Reduce heat and simmer for 10-15 minutes or until syrupy. You can make this ahead of time and refrigerate or serve hot over the pork.

To cook pork, preheat a grill pan or barbecue to medium high, brush pork with oil and grill, turning and brushing with additional oil and juice or vinegar until cooked as desired. Set on a bed of lettuce and spoon over the hot or cold relish.

# Pistachio Crusted Chicken with Fresh Peach Chutney

**Serves 4**

**1570** kilojoules/**375** calories per serve; **17g** total fat; **3g** saturated fat; **125mg** sodium

> 100g unsalted pistachio nuts
> 10 basil leaves
> 1 tablespoon orange zest
> ½ cup buttermilk
> 4 skinless chicken breast fillets, about 130-150g each
> ¼ cup low salt chicken stock (see page 12)
> juice of ½ lemon

**Chutney**

> ½ cup fresh orange juice
> 2 tablespoons brown sugar
> 2 peaches, peeled and chopped
> 2 tablespoons red wine vinegar
> dash Worcestershire sauce
>
> steamed basmati rice, to serve

Preheat oven to 180°C.

Combine the nuts, basil and zest in a food processor and pulse on and off until just combined, but still coarse. Tip into a shallow bowl. Pour the buttermilk into another shallow bowl.

Place the smooth side of the chicken into the buttermilk and allow excess to drip off, then press into nut mixture to coat firmly. Transfer to a lightly oiled casserole dish and pour in the stock and lemon juice. Roast for 30 minutes or until cooked through with no pink flesh inside. Test with a sharp knife – the juices of the chicken should run clear.

While chicken is cooking, bring the juice and sugar to the boil in a small saucepan. Add the peaches and cook until softened. Add the vinegar and sauce and cook until mixture thickens, about 5-10 minutes.

Serve the chicken over rice with the chutney on the side. This is great with fresh steamed green beans or a rocket salad.

# Thai Minced Chicken Salad

**Serves 4**

800 kilojoules/192 calories per serve; 5.5g total fat; 1g saturated fat; 455mg sodium

500g skinless, boneless chicken breasts, finely diced or
   minced
2 teaspoons brown sugar
1 tablespoon fish sauce
1 stalk lemongrass
2 teaspoons olive oil
1 tablespoon fresh chopped ginger
1 small bird's eye chilli, finely chopped
$1/3$ cup lime juice
1 teaspoon lime zest
2 roma tomatoes, seeded and finely diced
1 spring onion, chopped
1 lebanese cucumber, cut into thin strips
$3/4$ cup loosely packed mint leaves, torn into large pieces
crisp cos leaves, to serve
$1/4$ cup fresh coriander leaves, to serve

Cos lettuce (or romaine) is one of those
staples we've become used to all year round,
but its peak is in summer.
The crisp leaves make it an ideal base to
scoop up mounds of this salad, but you could
also use butter, radicchio, iceberg or other
large, crisp leaf lettuce. The flavours of
tomatoes, cucumbers and herbs in season
make this dish come alive.

Combine the chicken, sugar and fish sauce, cover and refrigerate
for 10 minutes to allow flavours to develop.
Remove the hard outer leaves of the lemongrass and slice
the white fleshy part at the base into about 1-2 tablespoons
fine slices. Place in a mortar and pestle and grind slightly
or crush with a rolling pin.
Heat oil in a wok or non-stick frying pan and saute the ginger,
chilli and half the lemongrass for 1 minute or until browning. Add
the chicken mixture and cook, stirring until meat is cooked
through and white, about 4-5 minutes. Transfer to a bowl and
toss through the remaining ingredients.
Place 2-3 cos leaves on plates or on a serving platter and
spoon over the warm chicken salad. Sprinkle over the coriander
and serve straight away.

# Stir-fry Chicken

**Serves 4**

**1655** kilojoules/**396** calories per serve; **12g** total fat; **2g** saturated fat; **345mg** sodium

1 tablespoon olive or peanut oil

1 tablespoon fresh chopped ginger

2 shallots

500g chicken breast fillets, trimmed of fat, sliced

4 cups chopped mixed beans, try snake, green, butter

2 tablespoons mirin or sherry

$\frac{1}{4}$ cup low salt stock (see page 12) or wine

1 tablespoon salt reduced soy sauce

2 teaspoons oyster sauce

2 teaspoons rice wine or wine vinegar

1 teaspoon cornflour

$\frac{1}{4}$ cup unsalted dry roasted cashews, optional

2 cups cooked steamed rice, to serve

Heat half the oil in a wok or non-stick pan and saute the ginger for one minute or until browned. Add the shallots and stir-fry for 1-2 minutes or until softening, then add the chicken and stir-fry until just cooked through. Remove from pan. Heat the remaining oil in the pan, add the beans and and stir-fry for 1-2 minutes or until tender crisp. Return the chicken to the pan and add the liquids. Cover and steam for 1 minute to reheat. Dissolve the cornflour in a tablespoon of water and pour into the wok, stirring until mixture thickens. Serve straight away on the rice.

# Marinated Beef and Nectarine Slaw

**Serve 4**

**1300** kilojoules/**310** calories per serve; **15g** total fat; **3.5g** saturated fat; **380mg** sodium

500g lean beef, such as fillet, rump, sirloin, any excess fat removed

**Marinade**

1 clove garlic, crushed

2 teaspoons fish sauce

2 teaspoons salt reduced soy sauce

$1\frac{1}{2}$ tablespoons brown sugar

juice of 1 lime

1 teaspoon chilli sauce or chopped chilli

**Salad**

4 tinned peach halves, or 2 fresh peaches, halved

1 lebanese cucumber, seeded and cut into strips

$\frac{1}{2}$ cup finely sliced fennel

$\frac{1}{4}$ cup each chopped fresh coriander and basil

few handfuls radicchio, frisee, curly endive, red cabbage, or preferred leafy vegetable

**Dressing**

1 tablespoon lemon juice

1 tablespoon sherry vinegar or red wine vinegar

2 tablespoons extra virgin olive oil

freshly ground pepper to taste

Place beef in a non-reactive bowl. Combine the marinade ingredients and pour over beef. Cover and marinate overnight. Preheat the oven to 200°C.

Tie beef securely with string. Sear the beef in a non-stick frying pan, then transfer to the oven to roast for 10 minutes for medium rare. Rest 5 minutes, then slice thinly.

Toss together the salad ingredients with the dressing. Arrange on plates and top with the warm beef.

There are many delicious summer fruits that work well with this slaw, such as mango, apricot or melon, but the plump summer fennel and cucumber are a must.

# Lamb with Balsamic Sauce, Fennel and Pumpkin

**Serves 4**

**1050** kilojoules/**251** calories per serve; **10g** total fat; **3g** saturated fat; **145mg** sodium

500-600g lean lamb loin
1 tablespoon olive oil
freshly ground black pepper
fresh rosemary sprigs, to garnish

**Glaze**
$3/4$ cup balsamic vinegar
1 tablespoon lemon juice
1 teaspoon sugar
1 sprig rosemary

**Fennel**
1 plump bulb fennel
1 red onion, cut into wedges
$1/2$ cup low salt stock (see page 12)

**Pumpkin**
2 cups chopped pumpkin
$1/2$ teaspoon nutmeg
pepper to taste

To make glaze, pour all ingredients into a small saucepan and bring to the boil. Reduce heat and simmer until mixture thickens to a thin sauce. Remove rosemary, cover glaze, and keep warm on a low heat.

Brush the lamb with oil and season to taste with pepper. Heat a non-stick grill pan or frying pan and sear the lamb on all sides until browned and cooked medium, about 4-5 minutes each side. Allow to rest for 5 minutes before slicing.

While lamb is cooking, remove the outer leaves of the fennel and slice the bulb thinly. Bring the stock to the boil and braise the fennel for 5-10 minutes, or until it is just starting to soften but still crisp. Keep warm. Reserve the stock.

Steam or microwave the pumpkin, mash and season with nutmeg and pepper. Add a little of the reserved fennel stock if you'd like the pumpkin softer.

Slice the lamb and serve over the fennel.

Drizzle with the glaze, sprinkle with rosemary sprigs and serve pumpkin on the side.

I can barely wait for the cold months for garden fresh fennel and the huge variety of pumpkins. Look for firm plump bulbs of fennel. I always choose a very orange jap or other earthy flavoured pumpkin.

# Lamb, Eggplant and Lemon Stew

Serves 4

**1410** kilojoules/**336** calories per serve; **16g** total fat;
**4g** saturated fat; **145mg** sodium

1 tablespoon extra virgin olive oil, plus 1 tablespoon extra
600g diced lean lamb
1 tablespoon plain flour
1 eggplant, cut into 2cm pieces
juice and rind of 1 lemon
250g mushrooms, chopped, (try swiss brown, portabella,
    button, or a mixture)
$1/2$ cup white wine
1 cup low salt chicken stock (see page 12)
flat-leaf parsley leaves, to garnish

Preheat oven to 160°C.

Heat an ovenproof pan over high heat. When hot, add the oil, and sear the lamb on all sides until brown. Sprinkle with flour and cook 1 minute, stirring constantly. Add the eggplant, juice and rind of 1 lemon, mushrooms and white wine and stir in well. Add the stock, bring to a simmer and cover with a lid. Bake for $1^1/2$-2 hours or until lamb is tender and cooked through. Stir the stew to distribute the juices a few times during cooking.

# Port Veal, Fig and Rocket Salad

Serves 4

**1045** kilojoules/**250** calories per serve; **8g** total fat;
**1.5g** saturated fat; **195mg** sodium

1 teaspoon olive oil
1 tablespoon chopped fresh ginger
500g lean veal leg or rump steak
$1/4$ cup port wine, plus a few tablespoons to drizzle
**Salad**
4 figs, cut into wedges
6 basil leaves, sliced
1 tablespoon capers
100g baby rocket leaves
$1/2$ cup sliced fennel
2 witlof, sliced lengthwise
**Dressing**
2 tablespoons sherry vinegar
1 tablespoon extra virgin olive oil
freshly ground pepper

Heat the oil in a non-stick pan and saute the ginger for 1 minute. Add the veal and cook for 2-3 minutes each side or until medium rare. Pour in port and remove from heat. Transfer to a ceramic dish and chill in the refrigerator.

The above steps can be done a day in advance.

Place all the salad ingredients except the figs in a large bowl and toss with the dressing. Season to taste.

Slice the veal thinly and arrange over the salad with the figs. Drizzle the extra port and serve with a crusty loaf of Italian bread or baguette.

Figs start to appear in late summer and continue into autumn. Buy them at their peak when they are succulent and juicy. This dish can also be made using dried figs that have been plumped in hot water and drained.

# Herbed Rack of Lamb and Carrot Chickpea Puree

**Serves 4**

**1470** kilojoules/**351** calories per serve; **15g** total fat;
**4g** saturated fat; **395mg** sodium

1 tablespoon olive oil
1 rack of lamb, 8 cutlets, trimmed of fat and skin

**Crust**
3/4 cup fresh breadcrumbs
1 cup parsley
1 cup mint
2 tablespoons freshly squeezed lemon juice and
  zest of 1 lemon
2 teaspoons green peppercorns or crushed pepper

**Puree**
2 teaspoons olive oil
1 white onion, peeled and diced
1 clove garlic, crushed
1 teaspoon cumin powder
300g carrots (about 2 cups diced)
1 cup water or low salt stock (see page 12)
310g can chickpeas, drained

1/2 cup buttermilk or low fat plain yoghurt
steamed green beans, to serve

Preheat the oven to 200°C.

To make the crust, place lemon zest and juice, and herbs in a processor and whiz until chopped. Stir through breadcrumbs and press on to lamb, reserving 2 tablespoons of the mixture. Place the lamb in an ovenproof dish, herb side up. (For extra flavour, I sometimes pour some white wine or water into the pan, so it doesn't quite reach the flesh, and a few sprigs of rosemary. It also helps keep the pan clean.) Place in oven and bake for 20-25 minutes for medium rare or until cooked as desired.

While the lamb is cooking, heat the 2 teaspoons of oil in a large non-stick saucepan and saute the onion, garlic and cumin for 2-3 minutes or until the onion is soft. Stir in the carrots and cook for another minute, then pour in the water and chickpeas. Bring to the boil, cover and simmer for 15 minutes or until carrot is tender. Drain and reserve liquid. Pour vegetable mixture into a blender with 2 tablespoons of the buttermilk and puree, adding the reserved liquid if mixture is too thick. Return to saucepan and keep warm until ready to serve. Add the remaining buttermilk to the reserved herb mixture to serve on the side.

Remove lamb from oven and allow to sit for 5 minutes before separating cutlets or, if serving on a platter, partially cutting through cutlets, so they are easy to pull apart.

Serve meat on a platter with beans, with puree on the side.

# Slow Roasted Pork Loin with Rhubarb and Celeriac

**Serves 4-6**

**1395** kilojoules/**334** calories per serve; **13g** total fat; **2g** saturated fat; **290mg** sodium

600g pork loin
2 tablespoons olive oil
2 tablespoons dijon mustard
1 onion
1 tablespoon chopped ginger
4 stalks (about 200g) fresh rhubarb, cut into
   bite-sized pieces
250ml beer

**Celeriac Mash**

500g celeriac (celery root), peeled and diced
1 tablespoon lemon juice
$1/4$ cup skim milk, or to taste
freshly ground pepper

Preheat oven to 150°C.
Trim any excess fat from pork. Heat 1 tablespoon of the oil in a large flameproof casserole and sear the pork on all sides to brown. Remove from pan and spread with dijon mustard.
Add remaining oil to pan and saute the onion and ginger until onion is starting to brown, add the rhubarb, cook for 2-3 minutes, then return the pork to pan. Pour over the beer and bring to the boil.
Place in the oven, bake for 20 minutes, then remove the rhubarb from the pan. Bake a further 10 minutes, or until pork is cooked through. Remove from oven and allow to sit for 5 minutes before slicing.
While pork is cooking, boil the celeriac until tender, drain and mash with the lemon, milk and pepper, adding enough milk to bring to desired texture.
To serve, remove pork from pan, slice carefully as it will be very tender (you may just rather pull it apart into chunks) and return to beer mixture. Place celeriac on plates or serving dish and spoon over the pork and rhubarb with some of the braising juices. This is great with a side dish of steamed spinach.

When buying fresh rhubarb, always remove the green leaves immediately, if this hasn't been done already in the shop. These leaves – and to a much lesser extent the stalks – contain toxins, which can be harmful if eaten.

# Brandied Beef with Artichoke and Horseradish Mash

**Serves 6**

1540 kilojoules/368 calories per serve; 15g total fat; 3.5g saturated fat; 210mg sodium

3 tablespoons extra virgin olive oil

1 onion, diced

600g diced lean stewing beef, trimmed of fat

300g mushrooms, sliced

$^1/_3$ cup flour, seasoned with pepper and/or mixed herbs

1 cup red wine

3 cups low salt chicken or beef stock

2 tablespoons tomato paste

2 bay leaves

10g porcini mushrooms, optional

$^1/_4$ cup brandy

**Artichoke and Horseradish Mash**

400g peeled jerusalem artichokes, chopped

200g peeled potatoes

6-8cm piece fresh horseradish, grated
   (or 1 tablespoon prepared)

$^1/_4$ cup buttermilk or skim milk

freshly ground pepper

Preheat the oven to 160°C.

Heat an ovenproof pan over high heat, add 2 tablespoons of the oil and brown the meat in two batches. Remove meat from from the pan and set aside. Add the remaining tablespoon oil to the pan with the onion and cook 5 minutes, or until the onion is soft, stirring frequently. Add the mushrooms and return the meat, with any accumulated juices on the plate. Sprinkle with the flour and cook 1 minute. Add the wine, stock, tomato paste, bay leaves, and porcini mushrooms. Bring to a simmer, cover with a lid and cook in the oven for 1-1$^1/_2$ hours, or until tender. While meat is cooking, cook the artichokes and potatoes separately in boiling water until tender. Mash or puree together with an immersion blender or masher. Stir in the horseradish and buttermilk and season to taste. Reheat and keep warm.

Just before serving add the brandy to the beef and spoon over the hot mash. A great accompaniment for the richness of this dish is crisp leaves of cos lettuce with a swirl of lemon and oil.

Be brave this winter and try some of the more unusual earthy flavours of cold weather vegetables, such as the two in this mash, to complement the rich beef.

# barbecues

# Moroccan Lamb Kebabs with Herb Yoghurt

**Makes 8 kebabs**

**640** kilojoules/**153** calories per serve; **7.5g** total fat; **2g** saturated fat; **65mg** sodium

500g lean lamb, choose from round, topside, loin or diced

**Spice Rub**

$1/2$ teaspoon each coarsely ground black pepper, ground cumin, ginger, paprika and cinnamon

1 clove garlic, crushed

2 tablespoons olive oil

1 teaspoon lemon zest

**Vegetables**

8 baby globe artichokes or 2-3 large artichokes

$1/2$ lemon

2 zucchini, thickly sliced

1 red capsicum, cut into squares

**Herb Yoghurt**

$1/2$ cup mixed fresh herbs, try coriander, chives, parsley, basil

juice and zest of $1/2$ lemon

$1/2$ cup low fat natural yoghurt

If using bamboo skewers, soak in water for 15 minutes to prevent burning. Trim the lamb of any excess fat and cut into bite-sized pieces. Make a paste out of the spice rub ingredients and massage all over lamb pieces.

Cover and marinate for 1 hour or overnight.

If using baby artichokes, trim the tips and hard outer leaves, cut in half and put in a bowl of water with lemon juice to prevent discolouring. If using the large artichoke, trim tips and outer leaves until almost all the green parts are gone and you have reached the tender heart. Cut in quarters, remove the furry inner part and woody stem and place in the lemon water.

Place either baby or large artichokes in a saucepan of boiling water with lemon and simmer for 10-15 minutes or until just tender. Drain and reserve.

To make the herb yoghurt, place the herbs and lemon in a small food processor or mill and process to a coarse paste. Add to the yoghurt and mix well.

Thread the lamb and vegetables alternately on to kebabs and cook on a hot grill, turning frequently until cooked as desired. Serve with the herb yoghurt and bread such as pide or pita.

I'm embarrassed to admit as a cookbook author that I'm actually quite a lazy cook and have always put 'mastering the art of globe artichokes' in the too hard basket, seeking safety in the can, heaven knows why. For this book I decided I just had to tackle the chore and was pleasantly surprised how simple it is and, best of all, how delicious.

# Watermelon and Tomato with Mint Fetta Dressing

**Serves 4**
280 kilojoules/67 calories per serve; **2g** total fat; **1g** saturated fat; **120mg** sodium

12 large vine-ripened roma tomatoes
$1/2$ watermelon, cut into wedges

### Mint Fetta Dressing
$1/4$ cup reduced fat fetta cheese
2 tablespoons red wine vinegar
juice and zest of $1/2$ lemon
$1/4$ cup chopped mint
1 tablespoon low fat plain yoghurt

Combine the dressing ingredients in a blender and whiz until smooth. Pour into a serving bowl and refrigerate until ready to serve. Grill the tomatoes and watermelon for 5 minutes, turning once. Serve with the dressing on the side.

# Marinated Prawn and Mango Kebabs

**Serves 4**
640 kilojoules/153 calories per serve; **1g** total fat; **0.5g** saturated fat; **480mg** sodium

20 large raw prawns, peeled, with tails intact
2 mangoes, cheeks removed

### Marinade
1 tablespoon honey
2 tablespoons orange juice
1 tablespoon salt reduced soy sauce
2 tablespoons finely chopped fresh coriander
few drops Tabasco or chilli, optional

Thread the prawns lengthwise on to individual metal or bamboo skewers. If you use bamboo, soak in water for 15 minutes first to prevent burning. Lay kebabs in a shallow dish.
Mix together the honey, juice, soy sauce, coriander and Tabasco and pour over the kebabs. Refrigerate for 30-60 minutes.
Preheat barbecue and grill kebabs for 1-2 minutes each side or until just cooked. Grill the mango cheeks separately, about 3 minutes, turning once.
Serve with crusty bread or barbecued potatoes and salad.

Whereas meat dishes are often marinated several hours, overnight, or even over several days, with seafood it's a different matter. The delicate structure of the flesh 'cooks' in the marinade, especially if citrus – in this case orange juice – is present.

# Grilled Scallop Wrap with Corn Salsa

**Serves 4**

**900** kilojoules/**215** calories per serve; **4.5g** total fat;
**0.5g** saturated fat; **210mg** sodium

16-20 scallops
1 tablespoon lime juice
1 tablespoon brown sugar
2 teaspoons crushed or grated ginger

**Salsa**

2 tomatoes, finely diced
4-5 fresh basil leaves, sliced
1 tablespoon marmalade or mild chutney, such as mango
2 tablespoons red wine vinegar
2 corn cobs, husks and silk removed
olive oil for brushing

4 large flour tortillas or lavash, to serve
4 tablespoons low fat plain yoghurt, to serve
mixed leaves or sliced iceberg lettuce, to serve

Place the scallops in a bowl or dish. Make a paste with
the juice, sugar and ginger and toss through or brush over
the scallops. Refrigerate for 20-30 minutes.

Combine the tomatoes, basil, marmalade and vinegar in a bowl
and toss well. Set aside.

Brush the corn with oil and barbecue, turning until golden
brown all over. Slice the kernels from the cob and toss
through the tomato mixture.

Cook the scallops on a lightly oiled flat grill plate on the barbecue
for 1 minute each side or until just cooked, but still plump and
moist. Remove from grill.

Place the tortillas on grill for a few seconds on each side to heat,
but don't toast them as they need to be still soft to wrap.

To serve, spread a tablespoon of yoghurt on each tortilla, place
a few salad leaves down one side, spoon over some salsa and
top with the scallops. Fold in ends, wrap and eat straight away. If
the scallops are very large, you may want to halve after cooking.

Fresh corn kernels can be rather difficult to
cut off a whole cob. When the cob is
halved across, you can place the cut sides
firmly on a board and cut off the kernels with
a sharp knife, standing the cobs upright
and slicing downwards.

# Barbecued Ocean Trout and Potato Salad

**Serve 6**

670 kilojoules/**160** calories per serve; **5.5g** total fat; **1g** saturated fat; **60mg** sodium

4 medium pontiac or red skinned potatoes, scrubbed
400g ocean trout or salmon fillet, skin and bones removed
1 large head cos lettuce

**Dressing**

1 spring onion or a few chives, finely sliced
2 tablespoons red wine vinegar
2 tablespoons buttermilk
1 tablespoon extra virgin olive oil
1 teaspoon dijon mustard
freshly ground pepper

Combine all the dressing ingredients in a screw top jar and shake well. Lightly steam or microwave the potatoes until just cooked, then slice. Brush barbecue with a little oil and cook salmon. Transfer to a plate and cover with foil. Barbecue the potatoes until golden brown and crisp on both sides.
Spread cos leaves on a platter. Flake salmon into large pieces and arrange, with the potatoes, over the lettuce. Spoon over the dressing. Serve with lemon wedges, thick bread and olive oil.

# Five Spice Pork, Coriander and Fennel Salad

**Serves 4**

885 kilojoules/**211** calories per serve; **6g** total fat; **1g** saturated fat; **255mg** sodium

500g lean pork loin, or leg steaks or fillet

**Marinade**

2 teaspoons honey
1 tablespoon salt reduced soy sauce
1 tablespoon red wine vinegar
1 teaspoon Chinese five spice

**Salad**

1 large or 2 small fennel bulbs
2 teaspoons fresh oregano leaves
juice of $1/2$ lemon
2 teaspoons olive oil, plus extra for brushing grill
1 tablespoon currants
$1/2$ bunch fresh coriander, chopped (or basil)

Trim any excess fat from pork and pat dry. Combine the honey, soy, vinegar and Chinese five spice in a flat based casserole or dish and mix well. Lay the pork fillets in the marinade, turn to coat both sides, cover and refrigerate for 1 hour or overnight. Turn pork over occasionally while marinating.
Remove outer leaves and green tops of fennel and slice bulb very thinly. Toss with the oregano, lemon and olive oil. Set aside. Remove the pork from the marinade allowing excess to drip off. Heat barbecue and brush grill with oil. Cook the pork for 3-4 minutes on each side or until cooked as preferred. For a moist result, don't overcook pork. It can still be pale pink inside. Transfer to a plate, cover with foil and allow to rest for 5 minutes. Slice thinly. Combine all the ingredients, including pork, in a large bowl and toss well. Serve warm.

# Barbecued Paprika Chicken and Mandarin Salad

**Serves 6**

**900** kilojoules/**215** calories per serve; **12g** total fat; **2g** saturated fat; **75mg** sodium

500g skinless, boneless chicken breast fillets
1 tablespoon olive oil
1 tablespoon orange juice
2 teaspoons paprika

**Salad**

2 mandarins or tangerines
1 small red onion, finely sliced
1/4 cup chopped kalamata olives
2 tablespoons sherry or red wine vinegar
1 tablespoon extra virgin olive oil or nut oil
1/2 teaspoon dijon mustard
4 cups mixed Asian greens (mizuna, tatsoi, mustard leaves, watercress or preferred greens)
1/4 cup unsalted flaked almonds, toasted

Place the chicken in a large flat dish. Mix together the oil, juice and paprika and brush all over the chicken. Cover and refrigerate for 1 hour.

Peel and segment the mandarins over a bowl to catch the juices. Put the juices in a small jar or bowl and set aside. With a sharp knife, cut the white pith from the mandarins and cut each segment in half from the centre to the peel side to make thin wedges. Place in a bowl with the onion and olives. Add the vinegar, oil and mustard to the reserved mandarin juice and mix well. Pour over the mandarin mixture.

On a preheated barbecue, cook the chicken, turning frequently until cooked through, about 10-12 minutes depending on the thickness of the chicken – there should be no pink flesh. Transfer to a plate and allow to rest for 5 minutes, then cut diagonally into large slices.

Place leaves in a large serving dish, arrange chicken on top and toss the mandarin salad and dressing through the chicken. Scatter over the flaked almonds and serve warm.

You can adapt this salad to the seasons: in summer try mangoes, peaches, apricots or plums; in autumn figs, kiwifruit or pears; in winter grapefruit, apples, pineapple or pawpaw.

# Field Mushroom, Lemon and Radicchio Burgers

**Makes 4**

**1265** kilojoules/**302** calories per serve; **5.5g** total fat;
**2g** saturated fat; **545mg** sodium

- 4 large flat field mushrooms, wiped clean and stems trimmed
- 1 lemon, peeled and thinly sliced
- 1 small red onion, thinly sliced
- 4 sourdough or gourmet hamburger buns, split
- 1 head radicchio, separated into leaves
- 2 tablespoons soft goat's cheese, such as chevre
- 4 teaspoons wholegrain or honey mustard

Place the mushrooms, stem side up, on a hot barbecue and cook until starting to soften and release juices. Place lemons and onion on grill and cook until browned on both sides.
Toast buns, cut side down on grill. Spread hot buns with mustard. Place a mushroom on one side, followed by the lemon, then onion and radicchio.
Crumble the goat's cheese over the top. Top with other half of bun and serve with a cold beer, red wine or sparkling apple juice.

# Balsamic Onion and Chicken Burgers

**Makes 4**

**2060** kilojoules/**492** calories per serve; **12g** total fat; **3g** saturated fat; **525mg** sodium

- 4 x 130-150g skinless, boneless chicken breast fillets
- 1 teaspoon olive oil
- 1 teaspoon wholegrain mustard
- juice and zest of 1 lemon
- freshly ground black pepper

**Balsamic Onions**
- 1 teaspoon olive oil
- 2 onions, sliced
- 1 tablespoon balsamic vinegar
- 1 tablespoon chopped parsley

- 4 Italian rolls, pide or preferred bread
- mixed leaves, to serve

Remove any excess fat or skin from chicken and pound with a mallet or rolling pin to about 2cm thickness. Combine oil, mustard, lemon zest and juice and brush over both sides of the chicken. Season with pepper and refrigerate until ready to cook. Preheat barbecue with a flat plate for the onions.
Add the oil and the onions to the grill and cook, moving with a metal spatula to stop sticking for 8-10 minutes or until caramelised. Transfer to a small bowl, toss with the balsamic and parsley and set aside.
Barbecue the chicken until cooked through but still moist – the juices will run clear when tested with a knife.
Heat split rolls on grill, top one side with mixed leaves and the chicken. Spoon over the onions and top with remaining bread.

*Balsamic vinegar and onions have a great affinity. The vinegar intensifies the flavour of the onions without overpowering their intrinsic sweetness.*

# New Age Patty Melt

**Serves 6**
**1405** kilojoules/**336** calories per serve; **12g** total fat; **3g** saturated fat; **350mg** sodium

750g rump or sirloin roast, trimmed of excess fat
2 onions, sliced
6 thick slices rye bread (or preferred bread)
2 teaspoons dijon mustard
2 teaspoons horseradish relish
40g fresh fat reduced mozzarella or bocconcini, thinly sliced

**Crust**

2 tablespoons fresh rosemary leaves
2 tablespoons coarsely ground black pepper
3 cloves garlic, roughly chopped
2 tablespoons olive oil
1 tablespoon grain or horseradish mustard
$1/2$ teaspoon garam masala or five spice powder, optional

Preheat a covered barbecue to medium high. Pound the meat with a tenderiser or, using a sharp pointed knife, make several slits over entire surface.
Make a paste out of the crust ingredients and brush over all sides of meat, pushing into the slits.
Barbecue, uncovered, for 3-4 minutes on each side until well browned. If using a coal barbecue, cover the coals with a barbecue plate so meat is not cooking over direct flame, and reduce heat. If using a burner, adjust heat so meat cooks slowly. Cook on medium heat, turning once or twice, for 15-20 minutes or until cooked as desired.
While beef is cooking, place onion on grill and cook until soft and caramelised.
Transfer meat to a plate and cover with foil for 10 minutes. While meat is resting, grill the bread until browned. Combine the mustard and horseradish and spread on to the grilled bread. Slice the meat thinly, catching the escaping juices. Lay bread on plates and cover with the sliced beef, pouring over the juices. Top with the caramelised onion and a slice of cheese. Allow cheese to slightly melt on the barbecue.
Serve with a huge garden salad and a bottle of red.

Based on the classic American patty melt with rye, minced beef, onion and cheese, here's a twist with lots more flavour and less fat. You'll need a covered barbecue for this dish, or start on the barbecue and finish in the oven.

## Red Wine and Honey Glazed Pears

**Serves 4**

**830** kilojoules/**199** calories per serve; **5g** total fat; **0.5g** saturated fat; **30mg** sodium

4 pears
2 tablespoons honey
¼ cup red wine
½ teaspoon ground cinnamon
freshly ground pepper to taste, optional
½ cup low fat vanilla yoghurt
2-3 tablespoons unsalted chopped toasted pecans

Preheat barbecue to medium high. Halve pears and remove core. Cut into thick slices. Combine the honey, red wine, cinnamon and pepper, if used. Brush some of the mixture over the pears. Place on grill and cook, brushing occasionally with the glaze, until golden brown and tender.
Serve with the yoghurt on the side, and sprinkled with pecans.

## Barbecue-steamed Thai Whole Fish

**Serves 4**

**960** kilojoules/**229** calories per serve; **4g** total fat; **0.5g** saturated fat; **480mg** sodium

2 x 500-600g whole fish such as snapper, bream, baby
    barramundi or 4 smaller fish such as rainbow trout,
    scaled, cleaned and gutted
2 stalks lemongrass, white parts only
8-9cm piece of fresh ginger
2-3 drops sesame oil
2 limes
1 bunch coriander
1 bunch basil
½ bunch mint
½ cup rice wine or sake
2 tablespoons salt reduced soy sauce
1 tablespoon plum sauce

Wash the fish thoroughly and pat dry. Make 2-3 deep slashes over surface and lay in a glass or ceramic dish.
Remove tough outer leaves of lemongrass and bruise with a rolling pin. Chop finely. Peel and chop the ginger into matchsticks. Remove the zest from both limes. Slice one lime into rounds as thinly as possible and juice the other. Combine the lemongrass, ginger, lime zest, lime juice, sesame oil and ¼ cup chopped coriander in a mortar and pestle and grind to just combined to a chunky paste. Divide mixture between fish, placing in cavity and over slashes. Lay a few lime slices in fish. Marinate in the refrigerator for 1 hour.
Cut 4 large pieces of heavy-duty foil large enough to completely seal fish, about 40-50cm. Arrange the remaining coriander, basil and mint leaves on the pieces of foil.
Lay fish on herbs and top with remaining lime slices. Bring together the sides and close securely, to completely seal, leaving one side open, to pour in the marinating liquid. Seal well after adding the liquid.
Preheat a grill to medium high and cook the fish for 10-15 minutes or until fish just flakes when pressed with a fork. Serve straight away.

# pasta & noodles

# Braised Lemongrass Turkey Balls

**Serves 4**

**1535** kilojoules/**367** calories per serve; **8g** total fat; **2g** saturated fat; **330mg** sodium

500g lean turkey mince, or chicken mince
1 tablespoon chopped and crushed lemongrass
2 tablespoons chopped fresh coriander, plus two
    tablespoons extra for garnish
2 teaspoons lemon zest
$^1/_2$ cup rice flour (or cornflour)
2 teaspoons olive oil
1 tablespoon chopped fresh ginger
juice of $^1/_2$ lemon
$^1/_2$ cup white wine
$^1/_4$ cup low salt chicken or vegetable stock

**Noodles**

100g thin rice noodles, soaked in hot water for 10 minutes
    and drained
3cm x 3cm fresh ginger, peeled and shredded
2 radishes, cut into thin strips
8 green beans, cut diagonally

Combine the turkey, lemongrass, 2 tablespoons of the coriander and zest in a bowl and mix well with hands. Shape into balls and roll in rice flour to coat.

Heat oil in a large non-stick pan and saute ginger and garlic for 1 minute. Add the turkey balls and cook for 2-3 minutes, shaking pan so they brown on all sides. Pour in the juice, wine and stock, cover and reduce heat to a simmer.

Cook, turning occasionally for 15 minutes or until cooked through and no pink meat shows in centre.

While they are cooking toss the noodles with the ginger, radishes and beans. Spoon noodles into pasta or soup bowls and top with the turkey. Spoon over some of the cooking liquid and top with the extra fresh coriander.

One of the delights of warmer weather beginning is getting into some warm/cold salad combinations like the hot turkey and cold noodles in this dish. It's also about enjoying the appearance of locally grown young beans and radishes.

This is also great with some chopped unsalted roasted cashews.

If you can't find turkey mince, buy turkey or chicken breast fillets and chop finely in a food processor with the other ingredients.

# Pasta with Prawns, Peas and Basil

**Serves 6**

**1690** kilojoules/**403** calories per serve; **2.5g** total fat;
**1g** saturated fat; **320mg** sodium

500g short pasta
1 cup fresh or frozen peas
 juice and zest of 1 lemon
$^1/_4$ cup water
500g uncooked peeled prawns (or use cooked prawns and
    add at the end)
small handful torn basil leaves or flat-leaf parsley, shredded
$^1/_4$ cup fresh low fat ricotta cheese
freshly ground pepper

Cook the pasta according to directions. In a high-sided frying
pan bring lemon juice and water to the boil and cook for
3-4 minutes to concentrate slightly.
Reduce heat and add the peas and prawns. Simmer for
2-3 minutes or until both are just cooked.
Remove from heat and stir in the basil or parsley and ricotta.
Return to stove to just heat through, then toss through the pasta.
Season with pepper and serve hot.

# Spring Vegetable Soba Noodle Salad with Calamari

**Serves 4**

**1630** kilojoules/**390** calories per serve; **8.5g** total fat;
**1.5g** saturated fat; **480mg** sodium

250g soba noodles (or angel hair pasta)
6-8 asparagus spears, ends trimmed and chopped
    diagonally
1 tablespoon sesame seeds
3 spring onions, dark green ends trimmed and
    chopped diagonally
2 tablespoons rice wine vinegar
2 tablespoons mirin or sherry
1 tablespoon salt reduced soy sauce
$^1/_4$ cup diced cucumber
1 stalk celery, sliced
400-500g calamari tubes
2 teaspoons olive oil

Cook the noodles according to directions on pack. Drain and
rinse well with cold water, separating noodles with fingers. Place
in a bowl. Plunge the asparagus into boiling water and cook
2 minutes. Drain and run under cold water. Dry on paper towels.
Toast the sesame seeds in a dry pan until light golden and
fragrant, about 2 minutes. Combine the vinegar, mirin and soy,
pour over the noodles and toss well to coat noodles in dressing,
then stir in the asparagus, sesame seeds and spring onions, as
well as the cucumber and celery. Set aside.
Score the calamari tubes in a criss-cross fashion. Heat the oil in
a clean non-stick pan and stir-fry the calamari for 1-2 minutes or
until just cooked. Take care not to overcook as the calamari
will toughen quickly.
Spoon noodle salad on to plates and top with the calamari.

# Angelhair Pasta with Fresh Tuna and Clams

**Serves 4**

**2405** kilojoules/**575** calories per serve; **7g** total fat; **1g** saturated fat; **285mg** sodium

375g angelhair pasta or preferred long pasta
zest and juice of 1 lemon
freshly ground black pepper
1 tablespoon olive oil
300g fresh tuna
2 shallots, chopped
2 cups white wine
500g clams (vongole)
2 tomatoes, diced
2 tablespoons capers
$^1/_4$ cup chopped coriander or parsley

Cook the pasta according to directions and rinse well. While pasta is cooking, combine half the zest with pepper and a little of the olive oil and brush over the tuna. Heat a large, heavy based frying pan, and sear the tuna for 1 minute on each side, then remove from pan and set aside. It should still be red inside. Heat the remaining oil in the pan and cook the shallots for 1-2 minutes, or until soft. Pour in the wine and add the clams. Cover, bring to the boil and cook until clams have opened. Remove them from the pan as they open and take the clams from the shell, making sure to save all their liquid. Give any that don't open a tap with a knife and if they still don't open after a few minutes, throw them out. Allow liquid to cook for another 5-10 minutes to concentrate. Flake tuna with hands or a knife. Add all ingredients to pan with the pasta, tuna and clams. Toss gently over heat to just heat through, making sure tuna stays pink and sauce coats all the ingredients. Serve straight away.

If you can't find clams in their shells, use mussels or buy tinned clams and add at the end on cooking. You could also use tinned, drained tuna for a quick pasta dish.

# Roasted Cherry Tomato Linguine

**Serves 6**

1340 kilojoules/**320** calories per serve; **4g** total fat;
**0.5g** saturated fat; **10mg** sodium

500g linguine or preferred long pasta
1 punnet cherry tomatoes, halved
8-10 basil leaves, sliced
freshly ground black pepper
1 tablespoon extra virgin olive oil
1 tablespoon balsamic vinegar
1 tablespoon lemon juice
few handfuls rocket leaves

Preheat oven to 190°C.
Line an oven tray with baking paper or foil.
Cook linguine according to directions and drain well.
While pasta is cooking, place the tomatoes, cut sides up, on oven tray and season to taste with ground pepper. Bake for 5-7 minutes or until hot and starting to soften. Tip into a large bowl and gently toss with oil, vinegar and lemon. Toss through the hot pasta and serve with rocket leaves on top.

# Zucchini and Peanut Pasta Salad

**Serves 6**

1435 kilojoules/**343** calories per serve; **11g** total fat;
**1.5g** saturated fat; **10mg** sodium

400g short pasta such as fusilli, penne, shells (conchiglie) or large macaroni
2 zucchini, thickly sliced
3 roma tomatoes, diced, or 1 cup cherry tomatoes
50g unsalted dry roasted peanuts, coarsely chopped
**Herb Vinaigrette**
2 tablespoons extra virgin olive oil
1 tablespoon lemon juice
2 tablespoons white wine vinegar
pinch mustard powder
1 clove garlic, crushed
1 shallot, finely chopped (or 2 tablespoons snipped chives)
2 tablespoons chopped parsley or basil
2 teaspoons dried chilli flakes

Place the vinaigrette ingredients in a screwtop jar and shake well. Refrigerate until ready to use.
Cook the pasta in boiling water until al dente, drain and rinse well with cold water. Cool and place in a large bowl.
Blanch the zucchini for 2-3 minutes or until just starting to soften. Pour into a sieve and rinse well with cold water to stop cooking. Allow to cool and add to the pasta.
Just before serving, add the tomatoes, peanuts and vinaigrette and toss well. Serve chilled.

My mum used to make this salad whenever we had visitors in summer, with fresh zucchini from the garden. There's nothing quite like the flavour of fresh small plump zucchini in season. Choose small,° dark green, firm zucchini with no wrinkling. For variety, you may like to try this with a mixture of green and yellow zucchini or substituting with other summer squash.

# Udon Noodles with Snake Beans and Sake Salmon

**Serves 4**

**1525** kilojoules/**364** calories per serve; **11g** total fat; **2g** saturated fat; **135mg** sodium

2 x 200g packets fresh udon noodles (unflavoured)
1 tablespoon peanut or olive oil
500g salmon fillet, skin and bones removed
freshly ground pepper
$\frac{1}{4}$ cup sake or mirin
4-6 long snake beans, ends trimmed and cut into
    bite-sized pieces
1 tablespoon toasted sesame seeds
few drops sesame oil
1 tablespoon julienned fresh ginger
2 teaspoons salt reduced tamari or soy sauce
2 tablespoons rice wine vinegar
$\frac{1}{4}$ cup low salt stock (see page 12) or water
coriander or basil leaves for garnish, optional

Pour boiling water over the udon noodles and loosen gently with a fork. Drain and rinse well.

Season the salmon with pepper. Heat a non-stick pan, add half the oil and sear the salmon, skin side down, for 1-2 minutes or until skin is crisp. Turn and cook for 1 more minute then pour in the sake and allow to steam for 1 minute or until nearly cooked, but still very pink inside. Transfer to a warm plate and spoon over the pan juices. Cover with foil.

Return pan to heat and add the snake beans. Stir-fry for 2 minutes or until tender but crisp. Remove from pan. Wipe down pan, add sesame seeds and cook, shaking pan until golden brown. Add the sesame oil, ginger, sauce, vinegar and stock and bring to the boil.

Add noodles and beans and toss well for 1 minute or until noodles and vegetables are heated through. Flake the salmon into large pieces Serve hot noodles straight on to plates, top with the flaked salmon, and scatter with coriander.

Snake beans, in season during autumn and summer, have a unique flavour and texture which is great with the Asian flavour of this dish. You can substitute with green beans, spring onion or other Asian greens.

# Mushroom Pasta with Basil Pinenut Crumble

**Serves 6**

**1585** kilojoules/**379** calories per serve; **6.5g** total fat;
**1.5g** saturated fat; **110mg** sodium

¼ cup pinenuts
¼ cup fresh breadcrumbs
2 tablespoons fetta
zest of ½ lemon
4-5 leaves of fresh basil, torn

500g bucatini or other long pasta
400g mixed mushrooms, roughly chopped
50ml white wine
juice of 1 lemon
1 cup sliced rocket leaves
handful basil leaves, coarsely torn

Combine the pinenuts and breadcrumbs and place on a lined baking tray. Bake in a moderate oven or under a grill until nuts are toasted. Add the cheese, zest of basil and grind in a food processor or with a fork to a coarse crumble mixture.
Cook the pasta according to directions. Meanwhile, heat the wine and lemon in a large pan and cook mushrooms until soft. Drain the pasta and toss through the mushroom mixture to heat through. Stir through the rocket and basil leaves and half of the pinenut crumble. Serve topped with remaining pinenut crumble.

# Thai Chilli Prawns, Chicken and Noodles

**Serves 4**

**2095** kilojoules/**200** calories per serve; **10g** total fat; **2g** saturated fat; **675mg** sodium

## Marinade

2 tablespoons chopped lemongrass, from the tender white part
2 tablespoons chopped peanuts
2 tablespoons chopped fresh ginger
1 hot red chilli, chopped, or to taste
1 sprig fresh coriander, root and leaves chopped
2 teaspoons lime zest
juice of ½ lime
¼ cup rice milk or buttermilk
½ teaspoon green chilli paste

400g green prawns, peeled with tails intact
1 large chicken breast fillet, cut into thin strips
green part of 4 spring onions, cut into matchsticks, for garnish, plus 2 spring onions, chopped
250g packet Thai rice stick noodles or wide rice noodles
1 tablespoon olive or peanut oil
¼ cup mirin, sherry or wine
2 tablespoons lite salt reduced soy sauce

Place the first 6 ingredients in a mortar and pestle and grind to a coarse crumb, or place in a plastic bag and pound with a rolling pin. Add to the lime juice, buttermilk and chilli paste and mix to a paste. Place prawns and chicken in a glass or ceramic bowl, toss with mixture and marinate 1-2 hours.
Place the spring onion matchsticks in a bowl of iced water and set aside for 10 minutes.
Soak the noodles in boiling water for 5 minutes or according to directions on packet. Drain well.
Heat oil in a wok or non-stick pan and cook the chopped spring onions until soft, add the prawns and chicken and stir-fry until cooked through. Add the noodles, mirin and soy, and cook, tossing and stirring mixture until heated through. Drain the spring onion matchsticks and use as a garnish.

# Spaghetti and Smoked Salmon Torte

**Serves 6**

**1000** kilojoules/**239** calories per serve; **11g** total fat; **3g** saturated fat; **405mg** sodium

150g spaghetti, cooked according to directions
1 tablespoon extra virgin olive oil
1 leek, cleaned and white part sliced
¹/₄ cup white wine or low salt stock (see page 12)
150g baby spinach leaves
50g black olives, sliced
100g smoked salmon, sliced into strips
6 eggs
¹/₄ cup low fat milk
freshly ground pepper
1-2 tablespoons shredded fresh parmesan cheese, optional

Preheat oven to 200°C.
Rinse the spaghetti well to separate the strands. Heat the oil in a large frying pan on medium heat and saute the leek for 1-2 minutes or until soft. Add the wine and the spinach and steam for 1 minute or until spinach is wilted. Remove from the heat and add the olives and salmon and toss to combine. Beat the eggs with the milk and season to taste. Pour the pasta mixture into a quiche pan or baking dish and pour the egg mixture evenly over top, shaking the pan to make sure the eggs cover the whole dish. Sprinkle with the cheese, if using, and bake for 30-40 minutes or until mixture is set but still moist. Let stand for a few minutes before slicing. Serving warm or cold.

# Sweet Potato and Broccoli Lasagne

**Serves 4**

**1440** kilojoules/**344** calories per serve; **12g** total fat; **4.5g** saturated fat; **500mg** sodium

**Sweet Potato Layer**
300g orange sweet potato (kumera or yams), peeled and chopped
2 teaspoons chopped fresh ginger
pinch of nutmeg
2 tablespoons buttermilk or skim milk
freshly ground pepper

**Broccoli Layer**
200g broccoli florets
3-4 basil leaves, torn
1 tablespoon lemon juice
¹/₂ teaspoon fresh thyme leaves
2 tablespoons low fat fetta

**Sauce**
³/₄ cup low fat ricotta
¹/₄ cup plain yoghurt or buttermilk
2 tablespoons low salt stock (see page 12)

9-12 square wonton wrappers
30g chopped walnuts
1 tablespoon grated parmesan cheese

Steam or microwave the sweet potato until just cooked. Mash slightly with the ginger, nutmeg and buttermilk. Season with pepper. Steam or microwave the broccoli until tender crisp then toss with herbs, juice and cheese.
Beat together the sauce ingredients.
Preheat oven to 180°C.
Lightly oil a large ceramic loaf tin or square casserole dish. Cover base with wonton wrappers. Spoon over the sweet potato mixture and followed by half of the cheese sauce and nuts. Cover with another layer of wonton wrappers and spoon over the broccoli and remaining cheese. Cover with wonton wrappers and sprinkle with remaining cheese and nuts. Bake for 25-30 minutes, or until top is golden brown and mixture is firm. Serve hot from the oven with salad, bread and olive oil.

# rice & grains

# Millet Cashew Crunch and Prawn Salad

**Serves 4**

**1700** kilojoules/**406** calories per serve; **15g** total fat;
**3.5g** saturated fat; **500mg** sodium

**Millet Cashew Crunch**

1 cup millet

1 cup milk

5-6 slices dried porcini mushrooms, optional

$^3/_4$ cup low salt stock (see page 12) or water

2 tablespoons flour

$^1/_4$ cup unsalted cashews, lightly toasted

$^1/_4$ cup chopped fresh coriander

zest and juice of $^1/_2$ lemon

1 tablespoon olive oil

**Salad**

2 teaspoons olive oil

24 raw king prawns, peeled with tails intact

$^1/_4$ cup white wine or juice (lemon, orange,
    apple, grapefruit)

100g salad leaves, rocket or baby spinach

**Dressing**

juice and rind of 1 orange

2 tablespoons rice wine vinegar

1 tablespoon plum sauce

1 tablespoon crushed or finely chopped fresh ginger

Soak the millet in the milk with the porcini, covered, in the fridge for 1 hour. Transfer to a large high sided non-stick frying pan, add the stock and cook, stirring over a low heat for 10 minutes or until most of the liquid is absorbed. Add the flour and cook for 2 minutes. The mixture should become quite firm. Transfer to a bowl and fold in the cashews, coriander and lemon.

Clean pan well and heat the olive oil. Add small firm spoonfuls of the mixture to the oil, making the crunch into 3cm rounds, and cook 2 minutes or until well browned, then turn and cook 2 minutes longer to brown both sides. It's OK if some fall apart – that adds to the crunch. Transfer to a paper towel lined plate and keep warm in a low oven.

While they are cooking heat the oil in a separate pan and saute the prawns for 1 minute, turn and continue until just cooked, then pour in the wine and steam for 1-2 minutes.

Place leaves in a bowl. Whisk together the dressing ingredients and toss half through the leaves. Arrange on plates or in a serving bowl, top with the warm nuggets and prawns and spoon over the remaining dressing.

I stumbled across this dish while trying to adapt my usual millet nuggets. The failure actually turned into success when everyone said they loved the crunch and texture and to leave it just as it is.

# Capsicum filled with Bulgur Salad

**Serves 4**
**760** kilojoules/**181** calories per serve; **6g** total fat; **0.5g** saturated fat; **10mg** sodium

2 large or 4 small red capsicums
**Filling**
$1/2$ cup bulgur
$1/4$ cup chopped parsley
1 tablespoon chopped mint
1 roma tomato, seeded and finely diced
2 tablespoons sultanas
2 tablespoons pinenuts, toasted
50g small ligurian olives
juice and zest of $1/4$ orange or lemon
1 teaspoon extra virgin olive oil

Preheat oven to 160°C. Pierce capsicum once or twice in stem end with a skewer. Place, stem side up, in a loaf or muffin tin so they stand upright and pour 1cm water in base.
Bake for 12-15 minutes or until just starting to soften. Remove from pan and cool. Place bulgur in a bowl and cover with boiling water. Cover and allow to soak for 20 minutes or until plump and tender. Drain and rinse well. Combine all filling ingredients with the bulgur in a bowl and toss well. Refrigerate. When ready to serve, cut capsicum in half lengthwise, scoop out seeds and white parts. Fill with bulgur mixture, pressing down well.

# Cracked Wheat Seafood Patties

**Makes 4 large patties**
**980** kilojoules/**234** calories per serve; **8.5g** total fat;
**1.5g** saturated fat; **300mg** sodium

$1/4$ cup cracked wheat
450g mixed fresh seafood, finely diced (try firm white fish such as ling or blue eye, scallops, prawns, crab, tuna)
2 tablespoons each finely chopped fresh coriander and parsley
1 spring onion, finely chopped
zest of $1/2$ lemon
2 egg whites
freshly ground pepper
$1/4$ cup dry breadcrumbs or panko (Japanese breadcrumbs), plus more for coating
1-2 tablespoons olive oil

Bring the water to a boil, add the wheat gradually, stirring constantly. When the water boils again, cover and simmer for 15 minutes. Stand 5 minutes to cool slightly. Transfer to a bowl, add all the other ingredients, except for the oil, and mix well. I prefer to do this with my hands to make sure all the ingredients are well mixed. Gently squeeze your hand through the mix, then shape into 12 small patties, or 4 large patties, if desired.
Place extra breadcrumbs in a flat bowl and coat patties, pressing well so they are firm.
Heat oil in a non-stick pan over medium heat and carefully add the patties. Take care, as they are crumbly until cooked. Cook for 2-3 minutes or until browned underneath. Turn and cook for another 2-3 minutes or until cooked through. Serve immediately.

These are great with just lemon wedges and a salad of rocket leaves.

# Sushi Salad with Creamy Wasabi Dressing

**Serves 4**

**1310** kilojoules/**313** calories per serve; **8g** total fat;
**1.5g** saturated fat; **35mg** sodium

**Sesame Rice Crunch**
>    2 tablespoons rice
>    2 tablespoons sesame seeds
>    1 sheet nori, toasted

**Salad**
>    1 cup short or medium grain rice
>    1$\frac{1}{4}$ cups water
>    $\frac{1}{2}$ avocado, diced
>    $\frac{1}{2}$ cup diced lebanese or telegraph cucumber
>    $\frac{1}{2}$ cup chopped carrot
>    $\frac{1}{4}$ cup pickled ginger

**Wasabi Dressing**
>    $\frac{1}{2}$-1 teaspoon wasabi or to taste
>    2 tablespoons mirin
>    2 tablespoons rice wine vinegar
>    1 teaspoon sugar
>    pinch salt, optional

To make the sesame rice crunch, heat a non-stick pan and dry-fry the rice, shaking continually until rice starts to brown. Add the sesame seeds and continue to toast, shaking pan, until both are well browned but not burned. Set aside to cool. Slice half the nori into thin strips and add to the sesame rice mixture. Cut the remaining nori into squares and reserve.

Grind the sesame rice mixture in a mortar and pestle or spice grinder to a coarse crumb. I sometimes use a well cleaned coffee grinder. Set aside. You could make a larger quantity of this and store in a glass jar in a cool place to use in other recipes.

To make the salad, rinse and drain the rice several times until the water runs clear. Allow to sit in a colander for 10 minutes. Transfer to a heavy based saucepan with a tight fitting lid and add the water. Bring to the boil, cover and simmer for 5 minutes. Turn heat to very low and allow to steam for 10 minutes. Remove saucepan from heat and keep covered for 10-15 minutes longer until all liquid is absorbed. Fluff with a fork.

Whisk together the dressing ingredients and toss through the rice, then gently fold in the diced vegetables and ginger. Serve warm or chilled. Fluff again with a fork before serving. Serve with the sesame rice crunch and the reserved toasted nori squares.

A twist on the classic sushi, and less fiddly. Summer's avocado and cucumbers are the perfect vegetables for this dish, but you could add any you like. It's fun having friends over and serving with halved nori sheets and some fresh-from-the-ocean sashimi to make your own hand rolls.

# Couscous with Mussels and Wine

**Serves 4**

**1375** kilojoules/**328** calories per serve; **6.5g** total fat;
**1g** saturated fat; **160mg** sodium

750ml bottle of white wine, try a big, fruity or grassy
   sauvignon blanc, chardonnay or riesling
2-3 cloves garlic, chopped
1 sprig fresh thyme
16-20 mussels, cleaned and debearded
1 cup couscous
3-4 finely diced tomatoes
$1/2$ cup chopped parsley
splash of olive oil, squeeze of lemon juice and
   grinding of pepper

Pour wine into a large heavy-based saucepan. Add the garlic
and thyme and bring to the boil. Add the mussels, cover pan and
boil for 5 minutes or until mussels have opened. Shake pan
a few times during cooking. Discard any that don't open.
Remove from heat, push mussels to one side and pour
the couscous into the liquid. Shake pan to distribute couscous
evenly through liquid and settle mussels evenly. Allow to steam
for 5 minutes, then scatter the tomatoes and parsley over
the top. Finish with a splash of oil, lemon and grinding of pepper.
Serve straight away from the pan with crusty bread and a salad.

# Roasted Corn and Couscous Cakes

**Makes 12 cakes**

**355** kilojoules/**85** calories per serve; **6.5g** total fat; **1.5g** saturated
fat; **20mg** sodium

$1/3$ cup dry couscous
2 teaspoons lemon zest
2 tablespoons olive oil
1 corn cob, husk and silk removed
1 teaspoon each olive oil and lemon juice
freshly ground black pepper
$1/2$ red capsicum, seeded and diced
$1/2$ avocado, finely diced
$1/4$ cup low fat ricotta
$1/4$ cup chopped fresh basil or coriander
2 eggs

Place the couscous in a heatproof bowl and pour over $1/3$ cup
boiling water. Cover and steam for 10 minutes, then transfer to
a fine mesh sieve and push out any excess moisture. Transfer to
a bowl, add the lemon zest and fluff with a fork.
Brush the corn with oil and lemon juice, season with pepper
and wrap in foil. Bake for 10 minutes, then cool and cut
the kernels from the cob.
Add to the couscous with the tomato, avocado and basil.
Beat the ricotta with a fork or beaters to fluff it up then fold
through the couscous. Beat the eggs and fold through
the mixture. Mix well.
Heat 2 teaspoons of oil in the pan and add $1/4$ cup of the
mixture, patting down to flatten cakes. Cook for 1-2 minutes or
until browned underneath and set enough to turn. Turn and cook
for another minute then transfer to a plate lined with a paper
towel. Keep warm in a low oven while the remainder are cooked.
Serve hot with lemon wedges or some tomato chutney.

# Polenta Shortcakes with Tomato Ginger Jam

**Makes 24**

430 kilojoules/**105** calories per serve; **2.8g** total fat;
**0.5g** saturated fat; **135mg** sodium

**Tomato Ginger Jam**

- 2 teaspoons olive oil
- 2 shallots, chopped
- 1 tablespoon chopped fresh ginger
- $1/2$ green apple, finely diced
- $1/4$ cup brown sugar
- 2 tablespoons red wine or cider vinegar
- 4 large or 6 small soft tomatoes, chopped
- 2 tablespoons plum sauce
- 1 tablespoon crystallised ginger, finely chopped, (optional)

**Shortcakes**

- $1^1/4$ cups polenta
- $1^1/2$ cups self-raising flour
- 2 teaspoons baking powder
- 2 tablespoons olive oil
- 1 cup skim milk
- 1 tablespoon lemon juice

low fat fresh ricotta, to serve

To make the jam, heat the oil in a saucepan over medium heat and saute the shallots, ginger and apple for 2-3 minutes or until soft. Add the sugar and cook for 1 minute. Add the remaining ingredients and bring to the boil. Reduce heat and simmer for 25-30 minutes or until thick and glossy. Cool, pour into jars or a sealed container and refrigerate for up to a week.

To make shortcakes, preheat oven to 220°C. Sprinkle a baking tray with polenta.

Sift the polenta, flour and baking powder into a large bowl. Make a well in the centre. Whisk together the oil, milk and lemon and pour into the well. Mix with a knife until mixture comes together. Transfer to a well-floured surface and knead gently to a soft dough. Press out with hands to a $1/2$cm thickness. Cut into 6cm rounds with a scone cutter or to desired size. Place in rows on baking tray with sides touching. Bake for 10 minutes or until golden brown. Serve warm or cold, spread with ricotta and topped with the jam.

These shortcakes can be frozen and reheated in the oven.

Tomato jam is a great way to use up softening tomatoes in autumn. You can make extra and refrigerate for using as a spread or topping for fish, meat or grilled vegetables over quite a few days.

# Warm Middle Eastern Barley Salad

**Serves 6**

**765** kilojoules/**183** calories per serve; **6.5g** total fat; **1g** saturated fat; **80mg** sodium

1 cup pearl barley
¼ cup sliced dried apricots
¼ cup chopped fresh chervil or parsley
½ red capsicum, finely chopped
45g (¼ cup) crumbled fat reduced fetta
2 tablespoons chopped fresh dill leaves or
   2 teaspoons dried
juice and zest of ½ lemon
2 teaspoons extra virgin olive oil
few drops truffle oil, optional
¼ cup unsalted flaked almonds, toasted

Boil the barley in water or stock until tender, about 35-40 minutes or microwave as directed on packet. Drain and rinse well.
In a large bowl toss together the barley, apricots, herbs, capsicum, cheese and lemon zest. Whisk the juice and oils together and toss through the salad. Sprinkle with the almonds and serve warm or refrigerate and serve as a cold salad.

# Wild Rice and Chicken Pilaf

**Serves 4**

**2130** kilojoules/**509** calories per serve; **11g** total fat; **1.5g** saturated fat; **95mg** sodium

1 cup (190g) wild rice
½ cup basmati rice
2 teaspoons olive oil
2 cloves garlic, chopped
1 white onion, chopped
400g chicken breast fillet, thinly sliced
1 cup low salt chicken stock (see page 12)
1 cup dry white wine
small handful basil leaves, torn
2 tablespoons unsalted blanched almonds, toasted and
   chopped, to garnish

Place wild rice and basmati in a pan of cold water, bring to the boil and simmer 5 minutes. Remove from heat, cover and allow to steam for 20-30 minutes so grains swell. Drain well. Heat oil in a large non-stick saucepan or high sided frying pan and cook the garlic and onion for 2-3 minutes or until soft and aromatic. Add the chicken and cook, stirring until chicken is browned on all sides. Add the rice, stock and wine, cover and cook 15 minutes, stirring occasionally. Cook until chicken and rice are cooked through and most of liquid is absorbed. Add a little more water or stock if mixture becomes dry before fully cooked. Fold in basil leaves, remove from heat and stand for 5 minutes. Serve pilaf in bowls and sprinkle with the almonds.

This is great with just plain yoghurt on the side and a crisp salad.

# Apple, Fresh Herb and Broadbean Risotto

**Serves 4**

2070 kilojoules/**495** calories per serve; **18g** total fat;
**3.5g** saturated fat; **130mg** sodium

**Parmesan Apple Chips**

1 small green apple
1 tablespoon extra virgin olive oil
1 teaspoon lemon juice
2 tablespoons shredded parmesan cheese
1 teaspoon lemon zest

**Risotto**

4 cups low salt stock (see page 12)
3 spring onions
2 tablespoons olive oil
1$^1/_2$ cups arborio or other risotto rice
1 cup apple cider or sparkling apple juice
10-12 large fresh broadbean pods, beans removed
$^1/_2$ cup loosely packed chopped fresh herbs, try basil,
    oregano, parsley, chives, mint
juice of $^1/_2$ lemon
lemon wedges and a rocket salad, to serve

To make parmesan apple chips, preheat oven to 190°C. Thinly
slice apple horizontally, pushing out seeds as you go.
Combine the oil and lemon and brush over the apple. Lay on
a lined baking sheet and sprinkle with the parmesan and zest.
Bake 5 minutes or until golden brown and starting to crisp.
Cool on a wire rack and set aside.

To make risotto, bring the stock to the boil, reduce heat and
keep warm. Remove most of the green ends from the spring
onion and chop the remainder. In a separate large saucepan,
heat the oil and saute the onion for 1-2 minutes or until soft. Add
the rice and cook, stirring for 1 minute, to coat rice completely.
Add the apple cider and cook, stirring until cider is absorbed.
Add the stock, a ladle at a time, stirring constantly and
allowing all liquid to be absorbed before adding next ladle.
It will take about 20 minutes. Just before adding last ladle, add
the broadbeans and cook in the rice.

When all liquid is absorbed and rice is creamy and cooked,
remove from heat, fold in the herbs and lemon, cover and allow
to stand for 2-3 minutes. Serve immediately, topped with
the parmesan apple chips, lemon wedges, and a rocket salad.

You can also use calrose rice, but you
won't end up with the creamy, plump texture.

# Beetroot and Red Wine Risotto

**Serves 4**

2000 kilojoules/477 calories per serve; 13g total fat; 3g saturated fat; 175mg sodium

2 tablespoons extra virgin olive oil

1 red onion, diced

1$^1$/$_2$ cups arborio rice

2 red beetroots, peeled and diced

1 cup red wine, try a shiraz, merlot or blend

4 cups hot low salt chicken stock (see page 12)

juice and grated rind of $^1$/$_2$ lemon

shaved parmesan cheese (optional)

Heat the oil in a large heavy-based saucepan. Add the onion and cook for 1-2 minutes or until starting to soften. Add the rice and beets and cook, stirring for 2 minutes or until rice is well coated. Pour in wine and cook, stirring until all liquid is absorbed. Add the chicken stock a ladle at a time, stirring constantly and allowing all the liquid to be absorbed before adding the next ladleful. Continue until the rice is creamy and al dente, about 20 minutes. Remove from heat, stir in lemon juice and rind, cover and allow to stand for 2-3 minutes. Season with pepper and serve with a few shavings of parmesan cheese, if you like.

# Polenta and Salmon Sandwiches

**Serves 4**

1025 kilojoules/244 calories per serve; 8g total fat; 2.5g saturated fat; 135mg sodium

**Polenta**

1$^1$/$_2$ cups cold water

$^1$/$_4$ cup low fat milk

$^1$/$_2$ cup polenta

6-7 pieces dried porcini mushrooms, chopped

3-4 large fresh basil leaves, torn

1 tablespoon shredded parmesan cheese

2 teaspoons extra virgin olive oil, plus 1 teaspoon extra for the salmon

150g mixed mushrooms, try oyster, shitake, swiss brown, button, halved or quartered if large

50g baby spinach leaves

2 teaspoons lemon juice

2 x 200-250g thick salmon fillets, bones and skin removed

5-6 basil leaves, torn, extra

1 tablespoon parmesan cheese, extra

Line a 22-23cm pan with foil and brush lightly with oil. To make polenta, whisk together the water, milk, polenta and mushrooms in a large heavy based saucepan. Place over a moderate heat and bring to the boil, whisking constantly and making sure polenta doesn't stick to base of pan. Reduce heat to low, and cook, stirring frequently, for 15-18 minutes or until thick. Fold through parmesan cheese. Pour into prepared pan, cover and refrigerate until set, about one hour. This can be made well in advance or the day before if preferred. Just before serving, slice into 8 triangles.

Preheat oven to 200°C.

Heat 1 teaspoon of the oil in a non-stick pan and cook the mushrooms for 2-3 minutes or until soft. Stir in the spinach leaves. Remove from pan and drain off liquid, reserving liquid and pressing moisture from mushrooms. Combine mushroom liquid with lemon and set aside.

Slice each salmon fillet in 2 horizontally to make 4 thin slices. Season with pepper and fry in a non-stick pan in the extra oil until just cooked, about 1 minute each side.

Grill the polenta on one side until golden, then sprinkle the other side with parmesan and grill until golden. Top each with a few basil leaves, then the wilted spinach. Spoon mushrooms over and top with another piece of polenta. Serve with the salmon and spoon over the mushroom and lemon liquid.

# vegetables & salads

# Piedine with Spinach and Mushroom Salad

**Makes about 5 x 20-22cm piedine**
**(or make smaller ones for snack size)**
**2200** kilojoules/**525** calories per larger serve of 5; **20g** total fat;
**3g** saturated fat; **155mg** sodium

**Salad**
2 tablespoons red wine vinegar
2 tablespoons lemon juice
1 tablespoon extra virgin olive oil
$1/2$ teaspoon salt reduced soy sauce
150g (1 cup) sliced mushrooms
250g (4 cups) baby spinach leaves
$1/4$ cup toasted pinenuts
$1/4$ cup currants
$1/4$ cup diced red onion
50g ($1/4$ cup) crumbled reduced fat fetta

**Piedine**
1 quantity yeasted dough (page 24)
polenta for dusting baking trays
1-2 cloves garlic, crushed
2-3 tablespoons olive oil
1 tablespoon lemon juice

Combine the vinegar, lemon, oil and soy and pour over
the mushrooms. Set aside. Toss together the remaining salad
ingredients in a large bowl and set aside.
Preheat oven to 220°C. Preheat non-stick pans or pizza stones
to fit the piedine dough.
Divide the dough into 4 or more pieces and roll out to
the thickness of a thin pizza. Dust preheated trays with polenta
and arrange the dough rounds. Bake for 6-8 minutes or until
just starting to brown but still soft.
Whisk together the garlic, oil and lemon for the piedine.
To assemble piedine, take dough straight from oven and brush
with the garlic dressing. Toss the mushrooms through
the spinach salad and place on hot dough. Serve straight away.
To eat, fold the dough around the salad and eat like a sandwich.

This is a great combination of pizza and salad
– a hot disc of dough wrapped around a cool
refreshing salad. Try with any of your favourite
salads, such as caesar, caprese, marinated
beef or whatever you fancy. Here, for spring,
I've used the tender young leaves of spinach.

# Asparagus with Goat's Cheese Sauce

**Serves 4**

**360** kilojoules/**86** calories per serve; **3g** total fat; **2g** saturated fat; **60mg** sodium

500g asparagus, trimmed
1 tablespoon flour, seasoned with pepper
1 teaspoon fresh thyme or oregano leaves or
  $1/2$ teaspoon dried
100ml white wine or low salt vegetable stock
$1/4$ cup milk (reduced fat works better than skim)
2 tablespoons soft goat's cheese, such as chevre

Steam or blanch the asparagus for 1 minute or until just tender but still crisp. Rinse well in a colander. Set aside.

In a non-stick saucepan, gently warm the flour and thyme, stirring with a wooden spoon until starting to change colour, about 1-2 minutes. Remove from heat and gradually add the wine while stirring. Return to heat and cook until thickened, then gradually add the milk, stirring until mixture comes to the boil. Reduce heat, add the cheese and cook for 1-2 minutes or until all the cheese is dissolved and the sauce is smooth. If you like a less thick sauce, add more milk.

Lay asparagus on a platter, and spoon over the sauce.

# Minted Spring Vegetable Stew

**Serves 4**

**With canned beans: 435** kilojoules/**104** calories per serve; **2.5g** total fat; **0.5g** saturated fat; **250mg** sodium
**With dried beans: 500** kilojoules/**120** calories per serve; **2.5g** total fat; **0.5g** saturated fat; **95mg** sodium

2 baby artichokes or 1 large globe
lemon
2 teaspoons olive oil
1 leek, cleaned and chopped
$1\frac{1}{2}$ cups low salt vegetable stock or water
1 fennel bulb, top trimmed and cut lengthwise into
  6-8 wedges
1 zucchini, chopped
425g can cannellini or white beans, drained and rinsed or
  125g dried cannellini beans (see box)
8 asparagus spears
$1/2$ cup peas
4 large cos or butter lettuce leaves, torn into large pieces
2 tablespoons mint sauce
1 sprig fresh mint, chopped

Remove outer leaves of artichoke, trim tops and base and cut into 4 wedges (or 8 if using a large artichoke). Cut out any hairy choke and place in water with a squeeze of lemon juice.

Heat oil in a large heavy saucepan and cook the leek until soft, Pour in the stock and bring to the boil. Add the fennel and drained artichoke, reduce heat, cover and simmer for 10 minutes or until artichoke is nearly tender. Add the zucchini and half the beans and cook 2-3 minutes. Add the asparagus and peas and cook for 1 minute then remove from heat.

Drain off most of liquid and place $3/4$ cup in a blender with the remaining beans. Puree until smooth. Pour back over the vegetables and add the lettuce.

Reheat and cook until cos is just wilted. Fold in the mint sauce and serve straight away, scattered with the mint.

For a lower salt alternative, soak dried cannellini beans overnight, or quick-soak. To quick-soak, cover the beans in a pan with 5cm water and bring to a boil. Boil 1-2 minutes, cover with a lid and set aside for 60 minutes.

# Tomato Ricotta Tart with Hazelnut Pastry

**Makes a 22-23cm square or rectangular tart, about 6 serves**
**1320** kilojoules/**315** calories per serve; **18g** total fat; **4.5g** saturated fat; **95mg** sodium

**Hazelnut Pastry**
80g ($^1$/2 cup) raw hazelnuts
1$^1$/2 cups plain flour
2 tablespoons extra virgin olive oil or hazelnut oil
$^1$/2 cup chilled skim milk

**Filling**
250g (1 cup) fresh ricotta
2 tablespoons chopped fresh basil or parsley
150g cherry tomatoes
freshly ground pepper to taste
balsamic vinegar and lemon juice, to serve
1 tablespoon fresh oregano leaves, to garnish

Place hazelnuts in a food processor and process until finely ground. Add the flour and process to combine. With the motor running, add the oil and then the skim milk, pouring slowly just until mixture comes together into a dough. Transfer to a floured surface and knead gently to a smooth dough. Wrap in plastic and refrigerate 30 minutes.
Preheat oven to 180°C.
Roll out pastry on a sheet of baking paper to a large rectangle or square, about 26-28cm. Trim edges to even out and brush along edges with water. Fold in about 1cm along each edge and then again to form a rim. Pinch corners and sides to seal rim into place. Lift the baking paper and pastry on to a baking tray and prick base several times with a fork. Bake for 15 minutes or until just starting to brown. Allow to cool slightly on a wire rack.
Whip ricotta with the herbs and spread evenly over the base of the tart. Place cherry tomatoes over the top and season with pepper. Bake for 15 minutes or until ricotta is just firm.
Serve hot or cold, drizzle with balsamic vinegar and lemon, and scatter with oregano leaves.

When buying ricotta, it's a good idea to buy a little more than the indicated amount, especially when you leave it to drain for a few hours in the fridge. You'll find that quite some liquid is released while standing, and you'll end up with less ricotta than anticipated. Weigh your ricotta just before using.

# Lettuce with Pear and Hazelnut Dressing

**Serves 4**

**565** kilojoules/**135** calories per serve; **12g** total fat; **1g** saturated fat; **10mg** sodium

1 large head butter lettuce
2 pears, diced (try white peaches in summer)
⅓ cup chopped hazelnuts
2 tablespoons sherry vinegar (or use champagne or
   wine vinegar)
1 tablespoon extra virgin olive oil
2 tablespoons buttermilk
pepper

Preheat oven to 180°C.
Wash and dry the lettuce leaves well. The dressing will coat
the leaves better if fully dry. Place the pears and hazelnuts on
a lined baking tray. Keep them separate so the pear juices don't
run into the nuts. Roast for 5-7 minutes or until nuts are
browned. Set aside half of each and transfer the rest to
a blender. Add the vinegar, oil and buttermilk and puree until
smooth. Season with pepper.
Just before serving, place leaves in a bowl, top with the reserved
roasted nuts and pears and spoon over the dressing.

# Hot Snowpeas, Mushroom and Basil Salad

**Serves 4 as a side dish**

**460** kilojoules/**110** calories per serve; **5.5g** total fat; **1g** saturated fat; **45mg** sodium

300g snowpeas
300g mushrooms, sliced (try button, oyster,
   swiss brown, shitake)
10 fresh basil leaves, torn
1 tablespoon extra virgin olive oil (or for a unique flavour try
   hazelnut, walnut or macadamia oil)
2 tablespoons balsamic vinegar
1 teaspoon salt reduced soy sauce
80g baby spinach leaves

Preheat oven to 190°C.
Snap the stem end from the snowpeas and pull away the side
string. Place with the mushrooms in a plastic bag and add
the basil, oil, vinegar and soy sauce. Twist end of bag and shake
well to coat all vegetables. Transfer to a baking dish lined with
baking paper. Bake for 8-10 minutes or until just tender crisp.
Serve hot, with baby spinach leaves.

This makes a wonderful side dish for grills,
spooned over rice, noodles or pasta, or even
as a warm salad with mixed Asian greens. For
the best results you'll need plump, moist and
crisp snowpeas. Test by breaking one in half.
They should snap, not bend.

# Pumpkin and Fetta Triangles with Macadamia Pesto

**Makes 4 pastries**
**1585** kilojoules/**379** calories per serve; **22g** total fat;
**4.5g** saturated fat; **545mg** sodium

250g peeled pumpkin, chopped
1 tablespoon fresh rosemary leaves, chopped
50g ($^{1}/_{4}$ cup) crumbled reduced-fat fetta
1 teaspoon cinnamon
16 sheets filo pastry
olive oil for brushing pastry

**Pesto**
35g (2 tablespoons) raw macadamias
1 cup loosely packed basil leaves
1 tablespoon grated parmesan cheese
1 tablespoon extra virgin olive oil
1 tablespoon lemon juice

One of the joys I get from cooking is creating dishes with someone in mind. To help inspire me for the book, I asked my stepdaughters to give me three ingredients they liked – for me to come up with a recipe. The ultra-creative Samantha brought me the challenge of pumpkin, cinnamon and rosemary and, thankfully, thoroughly endorsed the result though we switched from my idea of a soy-cinnamon glaze to a macadamia pesto which was meant to go with another dish! You could also add sliced mushrooms to the filling.

Preheat oven to 190°C.
Blanch or microwave the pumpkin with half the rosemary until just cooked, drain well and combine with the fetta and a pinch of the cinnamon, mashing slightly. Allow to cook for 10 minutes.
Lay 2 sheets of filo pastry on a clean dry surface (keep the rest under a tea towel to prevent drying out). Lightly brush with olive oil and sprinkle with a few of the remaining rosemary leaves and a pinch of cinnamon. Lay another 2 sheets on top and brush with oil. Cut the filo into 4 strips.
Place a quarter of the pumpkin mixture down one corner of the pastry, fold the corner over and continue folding to make a triangle. Brush with a little more oil and place on a non-stick or lined baking tray. Repeat with remaining mixture. Bake for 10-15 minutes or until golden brown. Serve hot with the pesto. These are also great served cold for lunches.
To make pesto, place all ingredients in a small food processor and pulse on and off until combined.

# Scrambled Egg Bruschetta with Grilled Tomatoes

**Serves 4**

**890** kilojoules/**213** calories per serve; **6.5g** total fat; **2g** saturated fat; **360mg** sodium

8 ripe cherry tomatoes, halved

4 eggs

1/4 cup skim milk

1 celery stick, finely diced

1 tablespoon chopped parsley

white pepper

4 thick slices Italian, wheat, sourdough or country bread

Grill the tomatoes. Lightly whisk the eggs with the skim milk, then stir in the celery. Heat the pan, add egg mixture. Cook over moderate heat, stirring with a fork, until just set, about 3 minutes. Stir in the parsley and season with pepper and keep warm. Toast the bread, spoon over the eggs and the tomatoes.

(PS This one's for you, Dad!)

# Insalata Tricolor Duo

**Serves 6**

**590** kilojoules/**142** calories per serve; **8.5g** total fat; **1.5g** saturated fat; **30mg** sodium

**Insalata Uno**

1 head radicchio lettuce

2 heads witlof (belgian endive)

1 bunch rocket

1 tablespoon extra virgin olive oil

1 tablespoon lemon juice

**Insalata Duo**

3 different coloured pears, try red bosc, sensation, william, nashi or your own choice

1/4 cup finely sliced fennel or radish

1 tablespoon soft goat's cheese

2 tablespoons buttermilk

2 tablespoons red wine vinegar

**Caramelised Pecans**

1/4 cup unsalted pecans

1 tablespoon brown sugar

Preheat oven to 180°C.

To make caramelised pecans, place nuts on a lined baking tray and sprinkle with the sugar. Bake for 5-7 minutes or until toasted. When cool, crumble pecans and discard excess sugar. Set aside.

Wash and separate lettuce leaves and dry well. Toss with the oil and lemon juice and arrange around a large platter.

Wash and slice the pears thinly and toss with the fennel. Beat together the cheese, buttermilk and vinegar and toss through the pears. Mound the mixture in the centre of the leaves. Scatter with the pecans and serve with a loaf of Italian-style bread and extra virgin olive oil.

I've rolled my two favourite autumn foods and salads into one with just a touch of fennel and goat's cheese for this palate-stimulating appetiser or accompaniment. It goes wonderfully with the Salmon on White Beans on page 40 or any grilled fish or meat. Choose firm bright radicchio heads with no brown edges, and not-too-ripe pears.

# Cardamom and Caraway Braised Cabbage

**Serves 4**

**440** kilojoules/**105** calories per serve; **5.5g** total fat;
**0.5g** saturated fat; **25mg** sodium

1 tablespoon olive oil
$1/2$ red or white cabbage or a mixture of the two (about
    500-600g), sliced
1 apple, grated
2 teaspoons cardamom seeds (you can also use
    ground cardamom)
1 tablespoon caraway seeds
1 teaspoon ground ginger
$3/4$ cup water
zest and juice of 1 orange
$1/4$ cup currants

Heat the oil in a large, heavy based pan with a tight fitting lid.
Add the cabbage and cook, stirring for 2-3 minutes. Add
the remaining ingredients and stir well. Reduce heat to low,
cover, and cook for 30 minutes, stirring occasionally and adding
a little more water if becoming dry.

This recipe is based on a Russian method for
cooking cabbage and brings wonderful
aromas through the kitchen, not the usual
'cabbagey' odour. It's a great winter side dish
for all kinds of meats, chicken or fish and
is also great cold.

# Citrus, Onion and Radicchio Salad

**Serves 6**

**305** kilojoules/**73** calories per serve; **3.5g** total fat; **0.5g** saturated fat; **35mg** sodium

2 navel oranges, or try blood oranges
1 pink or white grapefruit
1 lemon
1 red onion, peeled and sliced
2 tablespoons fresh oregano
1 radicchio lettuce or 1 curly endive

**Dressing**

2 tablespoons champagne or wine vinegar
1 tablespoon extra virgin olive oil
1-2 teaspoons green peppercorns to taste, rinsed
freshly ground pepper

Whisk together the dressing ingredients.
Peel the oranges, grapefruit and lemon and cut into thin slices, adding any escaping juices to the dressing. Toss with the red onion and oregano. Tear radicchio leaves into large pieces and place on a platter or in a bowl. Arrange citrus and onion salad over leaves and drizzle with the peppercorn dressing.

# Warm Brussels Sprout, Chickpea and Walnut Salad

**Serves 4**

**1140** kilojoules/**272** calories per serve; **17g** total fat; **2.5g** saturated fat; **170mg** sodium

16 brussels sprouts, stalk ends trimmed
1 cup cooked chickpeas (use tinned and drained, or for a lower salt version, cook your own)
50g raisins
50g unsalted walnuts
40g wedge salt reduced fetta or blue vein cheese

**Dressing**

1 lean bacon rasher
juice and rind of $^1/_2$ lemon
1 tablespoon extra virgin olive oil
1 tablespoon red wine vinegar

Cut a cross into the base of each brussels sprout. Cook in boiling water for 6-7 minutes or until just tender. Add the chickpeas to the water in the last 2 minutes of cooking to heat. Drain and keep warm.
While the sprouts are cooking, remove and discard any excess fat from the bacon. Chop bacon finely. Heat a non-stick pan and cook the bacon, stirring, until crisp. Remove from heat and drain on a paper towel. Whisk together the lemon juice and zest, oil and vinegar and add the bacon.
Transfer brussels sprouts and chickpeas to a bowl and toss with the dressing. Scatter the walnuts and raisins over the top and serve immediately with the cheese.

# sweets

# Pistachio Ladyfingers

**Makes about 30**

**140** kilojoules/**33** calories per serve; **1g** total fat; **0.5g** saturated fat; **10mg** sodium

$^1/_4$ cup shelled unsalted pistachio nuts
$^1/_4$ cup plain flour
$^1/_4$ cup cornflour
pinch of salt
3 large eggs, separated
few drops vanilla essense
$^1/_2$ cup sugar
pinch cream of tartar
icing sugar for dusting

Preheat oven to 180°C. Line 2-3 baking trays with baking paper. Place the pistachio nuts with some of the flour in a small food processor and process to a fine crumb. Sift together with the remaining flours and salt. Set aside.

Beat the egg yolks, vanilla and $^1/_4$ cup of the sugar with electric beaters until pale, thick and glossy. In a separate bowl, beat the egg whites until soft peaks form. Add the cream of tartar and beat for a few seconds, then add the remaining sugar. Beat until mixture is thick and glossy.

With a large metal spoon gently fold the yolks into the whites, followed by the flour, taking care not to over-mix.

Spoon mixture into a piping bag fitted with a 1-1$^1/_2$cm round nozzle. Pipe 8-10cm 'logs' on to prepared trays leaving 2-3cm between each to allow for spreading. Dust with a little icing sugar and bake for 6-8 minutes or until just starting to brown around the edges. You may need to rotate trays to allow even browning. Transfer to a wire rack to cool. Store in an airtight container.

# Strawberry Tart

**Serves 6**

**1770** kilojoules/**422** calories per serve; **24g** total fat; **6g** saturated fat; **135mg** sodium

**Macadamia Pastry**
1 cup raw macadamias, preferably pre-frozen or chilled
1 cup plain flour
$^1/_4$ cup cornflour
2 tablespoons sugar
1 egg, beaten
$^1/_2$ teaspoon vanilla essence
10-30ml chilled skim milk

**Filling**
1 cup (250g) low fat ricotta
$^1/_4$ cup light cream cheese
1 ripe banana
1 tablespoon icing sugar
1 teaspoon lemon juice
2-3 punnets strawberries, hulled

To make pastry, place the macadamias, flours and sugar in a food processor and process to a fine crumb. Add the egg and vanilla and pulse on and off until just incorporated. With motor running, add the milk in a slow continual stream until mixture just starts to come together. Transfer to a well-floured surface and knead gently to a soft smooth dough. Wrap in plastic and refrigerate for 30 minutes.

This can also be made a day in advance or even frozen.

Preheat oven to 200°C.

Lightly grease a large 32 x 11cm tart or flan tin. Roll out pastry to fit tin, trim edges and prick base several times with a fork. Bake for 12-15 minutes or until golden brown. Allow to cool.

In a food processor or electric mixer, whip the cheeses, banana, icing sugar and lemon until light and fluffy. Spread evenly on to pie shell and top with strawberries. Refrigerate till ready to serve.

Strawberries, especially when they first appear in spring, are irresistible, but you may like to combine them with apricots, or replace them with your own favourite fruits in this recipe – such as a combination of kiwi and pineapple, or apricot and raspberry, nectarine and grape, rockmelon and orange.

# Pineapple and Blackcurrant Sparkling Granita

**Serves 6**

**340** kilojoules/**82** calories per serve; **0g** total fat; **0g** saturated fat; **10mg** sodium

$^1/_2$ cup water

$^1/_4$ cup sugar

1$^1/_2$ cups sparkling wine or soda water

450g can pineapple pieces or 1$^1/_2$ cups diced
   fresh pineapple

blackcurrant juice concentrate for serving, about
   $^1/_2$ teaspoon per serve

Simmer the water and sugar in a small saucepan for 5 minutes or until you have a light syrup. Cool and add to the wine. Puree pineapple with $^1/_4$ cup of the wine mixture in a food processor until smooth. Pour into a bowl and mix in the remainder of the wine. Pour into a large glass bowl or baking dish and place in the freezer. Stir the mixture with a fork every half hour or so, until the mixture forms a coarse ice. You could also freeze in ice cube trays, then thaw slightly, turn into a bowl and mash with a fork. Serve in chilled glasses and drizzle with blackcurrant juice.

# Tangy Citrus Pots

**Serves 4**

**595** kilojoules/**142** calories per serve; **0g** total fat; **0g** saturated fat; **40mg** sodium

2 cups freshly squeezed orange juice

$^1/_2$ cup freshly squeezed lemon juice

piece of lemon rind

2 tablespoons sugar

$^1/_3$ cup cornflour

$^1/_3$ cup skim milk

$^1/_2$ cup low fat yoghurt

In a small saucepan bring the juices, rind and sugar to the boil. Remove from heat and remove rind. Dissolve the cornflour in the milk and gradually add to the juices. Return to a medium heat and cook, stirring continually, until mixture thickens and returns to the boil. Simmer for 2-3 minutes then remove from heat. Place in a blender, add yoghurt and puree for 10 seconds. Pour mixture into individual serving dishes or teacups, or one large bowl, and refrigerate until set and cold. Serve simply with a few raspberries. This dessert can be prepared the day before.

A perfect balmy spring dessert to use up those lingering winter navels and lemons. This one is for Emily, my vivacious stepdaughter, who, like me as a child, could eat her way through a lemon tree. Choose plump, tight, glossy navels for the best juice.

# Frozen Cappuccinos

**Makes 4**

**450** kilojoules/**107** calories per serve; **0.5g** total fat;
**0.5g** saturated fat; **70mg** sodium

1$^1$/$_2$ cups strong coffee, frozen in cubes
2$^1$/$_2$ cups low fat milk
sugar to taste
1 large or 2 small frozen bananas
nutmeg, cinnamon or cocoa powder

Place all ingredients in a blender and process until frothy and all
the cubes and banana are pureed. Pour into glasses and sprinkle
with nutmeg, cinnamon or cocoa. Serve immediately.

> I always keep frozen bananas on hand in
> the freezer to add body (and potassium) to
> smoothies, instant 'ice cream' or just to eat
> like an ice block. Kids love them, especially
> dipped in a little chocolate. Just peel and
> place in a freezer bag.

# Banana Nut Sponge with Mango Creme

**Serves 6**

**1735** kilojoules/**414** calories per serve; **20g** total fat;
**1.5g** saturated fat; **45mg** sodium

1 cup (about 150g) raw hazelnuts
$^3$/$_4$ cup plain flour
1 ripe banana
1 teaspoon lemon juice
1 tablespoon rum, optional
3 egg yolks
$^2$/$_3$ cup sugar
4 egg whites

Preheat oven to 175°C. Grease and flour a 22-23cm round cake
tin or line with baking paper and grease the base. Place
the hazelnuts in a food processor and grind to a coarse crumb.
Transfer to a baking tray lined with baking paper and toast in
the oven until lightly browned, about 3-4 minutes. Sift with
the flour into a bowl, adding the nuts left in the sieve. Set aside.
Process or mash the banana, lemon and rum to a smooth paste.
Beat the egg yolks and $^1$/$_4$ cup of the sugar until pale and thick.
In a separate bowl beat the egg whites until soft peaks form,
then beat in the remaining sugar until sugar is dissolved. Add
the yolk and banana mixture and beat for a few seconds until
just combined. Lightly fold in the nut/flour mixture with a large
spoon, taking care not to overmix.
Spoon into prepared tin and bake for 25-30 minutes or until
cake springs back when lightly pressed. Allow to cool in pan for
10 minutes then transfer to a wire rack to finish cooling. When
cool cut through the centre with a serrated knife and fill with
the mango creme.

### Mango Creme

2 tablespoons cornflour
1 cup mango flesh
1 tablespoon sugar, optional
few drops lemon juice
2 tablespoons creme fraiche or marscarpone

Dissolve the cornflour in 2 tablespoons of cold water and set
aside. Puree the mango flesh and place in a saucepan with
the sugar. Heat until mixture just comes to the boil. Remove from
heat and fold in the cornflour mixture and lemon. Return to heat
and cook, stirring, until mixture thickens and comes to a simmer.
Transfer to a bowl and fold in the creme fraiche. Allow to cool
slightly before spreading on the cake.

# Pawpaw and Orange Frappe

Makes 2

425 kilojoules/101 calories per serve; 0.5g total fat;
0.5g saturated fat; 65mg sodium

1 cup chopped pawpaw
juice of $^1/_2$ lime
1 cup orange juice
$^1/_2$ cup soda or mineral water
$^1/_2$ cup low fat natural or fruit yoghurt
6-8 ice cubes
3-4 mint leaves, optional

Place all ingredients in a food processor and blend until smooth,
adding more mineral water or juice if you want a less thick drink.
Serve immediately.

Try with any of your favourite fruits such as
melon, berries, peaches or kiwi. For an extra
creamy frappe, first freeze the pawpaw.

# Summer Fruit Mille-Feuille

Serves 4

1725 kilojoules/412 calories per serve; 25g total fat; 7g saturated
fat; 305mg sodium

**Pastry**

$^1/_2$ cup finely chopped unsalted nuts, try hazelnuts,
almonds or macadamias
2 tablespoons caster sugar
1 teaspoon nutmeg or cinnamon
4 sheets filo pastry
1 tablespoon light olive or canola oil

**Filling**

250g fresh low fat ricotta
100g light cream cheese
$^1/_2$ teaspoon orange flower water or vanilla
1-2 tablespoons icing sugar, or to taste, extra
1 teaspoon grated orange zest
2 cups mixed summer fruit, such as blueberries and
raspberries, or try apricot, pawpaw or
peach, or fruit in season
icing sugar for dusting, optional

Preheat oven to 175°C.
Combine the nuts, sugar and nutmeg in a small bowl. Lay
2 sheets of filo pastry on a clean, dry surface. Brush lightly with
oil and scatter with half the nut mixture. Lay another 2 sheets on
top and brush again. Sprinkle top with remaining nuts. Cut stack
into 12 triangles or squares and place on lined baking trays.
Bake for 10-12 minutes or until golden brown. Transfer to a wire
rack to cool. These can be stored for 1-2 days in an airtight
container. Whip together the ricotta cheese, cream cheese,
vanilla and icing sugar until light and fluffy.
To serve, place a filo triangle on each plate, top with a spoon
of the whipped cheese mixture, and scatter with some
chopped fruit. Repeat, then top with last triangle. If desired, dust
mille-feuille with icing sugar just before serving.
Note: Using fresh ricotta from the delicatessen will give you
the creamiest and smoothest filling.

# Cappuccino Mousse

**Serves 6**

**275** kilojoules/**66** calories per serve; **2g** total fat; **1.5g** saturated fat; **60mg** sodium

**Coffee Layer**

   1 sachet gelatine

   3 tablespoons water

   1 cup strong coffee sweetened with 2 teaspoons sugar (it's better to make the real thing rather than instant)

   $^1/_4$ cup milk

**Creme Layer**

   1 teaspoon gelatine

   $^1/_4$ cup low fat milk

   $^1/_2$ cup fresh low fat ricotta

   1 tablespoon icing sugar

   $^1/_4$ teaspoon vanilla essence

   cocoa powder for dusting

Coffee Layer: Sprinkle the gelatine over the water and set over a bowl of hot water until dissolved. Combine the sweetened coffee and milk and stir in the dissolved gelatine. Divide mixture between 6 coffee cups and refrigerate until set, about 1 hour.
Creme Layer: Sprinkle the gelatin over half of the milk and set over a bowl of hot water until dissolved. With electric beaters or a food processor, whip the ricotta, sugar and vanilla until light and fluffy, beat in the remaining milk and dissolved gelatine. Gently spoon over the coffee layer and dust with a little cocoa powder. Refrigerate until set. Can be made a day ahead.

# Autumn Harvest Cream Cheese Loaf

**Makes 24 slices**

**420** kilojoules/**100** calories per serve; **3g** total fat; **1g** saturated fat; **120mg** sodium

   1 large apple in season, grated

   1 large pear in season, grated

   1 large carrot, peeled and grated (about 1 cup grated)

   juice and zest of $^1/_2$ lemon

   $^1/_3$ cup finely diced or ground unsalted almonds or hazelnuts

   225g low fat cream cheese

   $^1/_2$ cup brown sugar

   2 eggs, lightly beaten

   2 cups sifted self-raising flour

Preheat oven to 180°C. Grease and dust a 22-24cm loaf tin or similar sized cake tin with flour.
In a large bowl, toss the grated apple, pear and carrot, lemon juice and zest, and nuts together. In a separate bowl, beat the cream cheese and sugar with electric beaters until light and creamy. Gradually add the eggs while beating, and beat another minute. Lightly fold this into the apple mixture. Add the flour and mix lightly to combine. Spoon batter into prepared tin and bake for 50-60 minutes or until a skewer inserted in the centre comes out clean. Allow to cool for 5-10 minutes in tin before turning on to a wire rack. Serve warm from the oven or store in a sealed container in a cool place, or the fridge, for up to a week.

You could really make this cake for any season, using whatever is available and fresh from the markets.
Try apricots and zucchini in summer, rhubarb and pumpkin in winter. It is delicious toasted and spread with jam or ricotta.

# Minted Nuts

**Serves 6**
**890** kilojoules/**212** calories per serve; **17g** total fat; **2g** saturated fat; **5mg** sodium

1 cup unsalted nuts, try macadamias and almonds
1/3 cup honey
1/2 cup cornflour
1/2 cup icing sugar
few drops peppermint essence

Preheat oven to 180°C. Roast nuts for 5 minutes or until you can smell the aroma, and they are becoming golden. While they are roasting melt the honey in a large dish in the microwave or on the stove until very runny. Place the hot roasted nuts in the honey and stir to coat well. Pour into a sieve and shake to allow all excess honey to drain off.

In a large clean plastic bag shake the cornflour and icing sugar. Add the peppermint essence and shake well again to distribute the mint. Take care not to add too much as it is quite strong. Add the nuts, seal the bag and shake, tossing so all the nuts become evenly coated.

Tip into a clean, dry sieve and shake gently so nuts remain in sieve and excess sugar and cornflour are discarded. Transfer on to a paper towel or a fine mesh wire rack to dry out and cool completely before sealing.

# Fig and Pecan Torte

**Serves 6**
**1575** kilojoules/**377** calories per serve; **21g** total fat; **1.5g** saturated fat; **50mg** sodium

175g dried figs, look for plump moist ones
1 cup water
175g unsalted pecans, toasted
1/2 cup plain flour
4 egg whites
1/2 cup sugar

Preheat oven to 175°C. Lightly grease, flour and line base of a 20cm square cake tin.

Place the figs and water in a small saucepan and bring to the boil. Cover and simmer for 10 minutes or until figs are soft. Strain the figs and process to a puree in a processor. Don't worry if some of the seeds remain. You should have about 1/2 cup paste.

Place the flour and pecans in a food processor and pulse on and off until the mixture is a coarse even crumb. With electric mixers, beat the egg whites until soft peaks form. Gradually add the sugar, beating until mixture is thick and glossy. Lightly fold in the fig paste and pecan flour.

Spoon into prepared tin and bake for 20 minutes or until cake springs back when gently pressed with a finger. Allow to cool in tin for 5-10 minutes before turning on to a wire rack to finish cooling. If desired, dust with a little icing sugar. Great with low fat vanilla ice cream or just by itself.

I created this torte for my wonderful father-in-law, Steve, who showed me the joy of stuffing dried figs or fig Newtons with roasted pecans. Yum!

# Almond Shortbread

**Makes 20 biscuits**

**310** kilojoules/**74** calories per serve; **3.5g** total fat; **0.5g** saturated fat; **15mg** sodium

100g unsalted almonds
50g marzipan or almond paste
1/4 cup self-raising flour
1/2 cup plain flour, plus extra for dusting
1/3 cup sugar
1/2 teaspoon vanilla
1 egg
2-3 tablespoons skim milk

Preheat oven to 190°C. Line a baking tray with baking paper or lightly brush with oil.

Place the almonds and marzipan in a food processor and process to a fine powder. Add the flours and sugar and process until combined. Add the egg and vanilla, then gradually pour in the milk with the motor running until mixture starts to clump. Transfer to a bowl and mix with hands to a dough – it will be quite moist.

Shape into teaspoon-sized balls and roll in flour. Place on prepared tray and press down gently with a fork. Bake for 12-15 minutes or until golden. Lift one and check the base to test. Cool on wire racks before placing in sealed containers.

# Apple Lemon Souffle

**Serves 6**

**390** kilojoules/**93** calories per serve; **0.5g** total fat; **0.5g** saturated fat; **30mg** sodium

2 small granny smith apples, peeled and diced
1 tablespoon lemon juice
2 teaspoons lemon zest
1 tablespoon plain flour
3 egg whites
1/3 cup sugar
1/2 teaspoon cinnamon
2 tablespoons icing sugar

Heat oven to 190°C. Grease a 20cm souffle dish or 6 individual ovenproof dishes and dust with a little sugar.

Blanch or microwave apples in a little water until soft, puree and allow to cool. Stir in the lemon juice and zest.

In a large mixing bowl, beat the egg whites with an electric mixer until soft peaks form. Gradually add the sugar and beat until sugar is dissolved and mixture is glossy. Add the apple mixture and flour and beat a few seconds just to combine or fold through with a metal spoon.

Spoon into souffle dish(es) and bake for 15-20 minutes for the large dish, or 6-7 minutes for the individual dishes, or until souffle is set and starting to become a pale golden colour. Combine the cinnamon and sugar and sift over the top.

I created this dish for my stepdaughter Sam who wanted a dish made with apples, lemon and cinnamon that was light and tangy and 'sort of like' lemon meringue pie! This was my attempt, which we discovered was light and fluffy, and warming straight from the oven. But when we allowed it to settle and tried it only just warm, the chewiness and resulting syrup were very appealing too. It's great in the colder months when tart apples and lemons are at their peak.

# Chamomile Rice Pudding

**Serves 6**

**835** kilojoules/**200** calories per serve; **0.5g** total fat; **0.5g** saturated fat; **8.5mg** sodium

4$^1$/$_2$ cups low fat or skim milk

4 chamomile tea bags

$^3$/$_4$ cup short or medium grain rice

$^1$/$_4$ cup sugar, or to taste

$^1$/$_4$ cup currants, optional

$^1$/$_2$ teaspoon vanilla and/or 1 cinnamon stick

3 mandarins or tangerines, optional

In a heavy-based saucepan, gently heat milk over a low heat until just starting to foam, stirring occasionally to prevent sticking to the base. Remove from heat, add tea bags, cover and allow to steep for 1 hour, or overnight.

Remove tea bags, add rice, sugar, currants and vanilla or cinnamon stick and return to low heat. Cook for 20-25 minutes, stirring occasionally to prevent rice from sticking, or until rice is cooked and mixture is thickening. Serve rice warm into bowls and top with mandarin segments, if you like.

# Sweet Potato and Pear Crumble

**Serves 6**

**910** kilojoules/**218** calories per serve; **6.5g** total fat; **0.5g** saturated fat; **15mg** sodium

1 cup orange juice

2 tablespoons sugar

500g sweet potato, cut into 2cm cubes

1 cinnamon stick

2 pears, peeled and cut into wedges

1 teaspoon ground ginger

2 teaspoons lemon zest

**Crumble Topping**

50g unsalted walnuts

$^1$/$_2$ cup rolled oats

1 tablespoon brown sugar

$^1$/$_2$ teaspoon cinnamon

2 teaspoons chopped crystallised ginger

Preheat oven to 175°C.

Bring the orange juice to a boil, add the sugar, sweet potato and cinnamon stick. Reduce heat and simmer until tender, about 10-15 minutes. Remove cinnamon stick and stir in the pears, ginger and zest. Pour the mixture into a large baking dish.

Place all the crumble ingredients in a food processor and pulse on and off until just mixed but still chunky. Spoon over the sweet potato mixture, nestling crumble down among the mix a little. Bake for 20 minutes or until golden brown.

# seasonal sensations

Each season brings with it a new taste that seems just right for the weather. Of course, seasons

vary depending on where you live. If you're in the tropics, for instance, you'll have a year-round

abundance of wonderful exotic fruit. Or perhaps you live in a climate with a long cold winter and

have the advantage of tangy firm navel oranges for an extended growing season.

The ideas on the opposite page are for a climate of four distinct seasons, so you may need to

adapt them to suit your own local seasonality. Explore farmer's or seafood markets to capture what

fresh and exciting produce and crops are 'fresh from the source' – experience their true flavours.

## spring

Barbecue plump firm **asparagus** spears and sprinkle with goat's cheese, roasted hazelnuts and a drizzle of balsamic vinegar.

Lightly blanch some **fresh shelled peas** in a little wine or lemon juice with **spring onion** and **mint,** to serve with grilled fish, chicken or **spring lamb**.

Steam **broadbeans** and puree with some buttermilk and pepper as a delightful sauce for pasta, over grilled chicken or salmon or steamed **artichokes**.

Toss **sugar snap peas** through Asian noodles with **watercress, baby garlic** and **ginger** and add a splash of rice wine vinegar, soy and a few drops of sesame oil.

Soak **peaches** in Amaretto and sprinkle with toasted sliced unsalted almonds and ricotta.

Capture the flavour of the first **strawberries** and fold through frozen yoghurt, or freeze for a smoothie.

Toss fresh **baby spinach** with sauteed **cepes** or **wild mushrooms**, currants, fetta and crumbled unsalted pecans. Or add a splash of colour with some sliced pink grapefruit.

## summer

Freeze **grapes** to nibble after meals instead of a heavy dessert. **Watermelon** and **rockmelon** wedges are also great frozen.

For a light summer lunch try **heirloom tomatoes** with moist fresh slices of mozzarella, **basil** and a drizzle of fruit olive oil, along with a crisp baguette and **rocket leaves**.

Toss sliced **fresh figs** with mixed **lettuce** with a sherry vinaigrette and top with some sliced rare beef or parmesan cheese.

Blanch thick slices of **zucchini**, chill, and toss through short pasta with **lemon, basil** and pepper for a delicious salad.

Roast **corn on the cob**, then slice off and toss through Israeli toasted couscous with fresh **apricots, mint, capsicum** and a few drops of truffle oil.

Freeze **bananas** for making huge smoothies with fresh **berries** and orange or pineapple juice.

Make a tangy salsa for barbecue prawns with **mango, cucumber, roma tomatoes** and **coriander**.

Give the kids a big bowl of **cherries** and sliced **nectarine**.

## autumn

Poach a **pear** in some red wine and serve with a dollop of honeyed ricotta.

Make a warm salad of steamed **brussels sprouts** and roast unsalted hazelnuts. Toss through cool **mandarin** segments.

Grill slices of **lemon** till just soft and serve on top of grilled fish fillet of your choice or **field mushrooms**.

Core out the centre of **green apples**, fill with currants, unsalted walnuts and brown sugar and bake until golden brown. Or be adventurous and add some chopped **persimmon**.

Start the day with a refreshing and nutritious dish of fresh **pawpaw** and **lime juice**.

Boil **broccoli**, then puree to a rich creamy soup with a few spoons of **avocado** and skim milk.

Roast freshly shelled almonds or macadamias and crumble over steamed **beans** and sliced **nashi** or **red pear** for an exotic salad.

Grill slices of **eggplant, sweet potato** and **leek** for a great variation of veggie burger.

## winter

Roast whole **beetroot** in foil, peel, dice and toss warm through some crisp **rocket leaves** with a dressing of unsalted macadamias and red wine.

Cook **artichokes** in boiling lemon water, then puree the hearts with white beans and lemon for a creamy dip or sauce.

Nestle grilled lamb or beef into a bed of mashed **celery root** or **celeriac** and drizzle with some concentrated balsamic vinegar.

Add sliced **rhubarb** to risotto and top with shaved **fennel**, parmesan cheese and lemon zest.

Braise **cabbage** with caraway seeds and grated **apple** to serve with a hearty bean stew.

Grill sliced **pineapple** and toss with rum and honey, then top with a scoop of low fat ice cream.

Grate fresh **horseradish** with **potatoes** to make zesty pancakes for a warming supper among friends.

Pan-fry halved **witlof** with segments of **tangelo** and toss with a splash of oil and some raisins.

# measurements & conversions

## Metric cup and spoon sizes

Measurements used in this book refer to
the standard metric cup and spoon sets approved
by the Standards Association of Australia.
A basic metric cup set consists of:
1 cup, $^1/_2$ cup, $^1/_3$ cup and $^1/_4$ cup sizes.
The basic spoon set comprises:
1 tablespoon, 1 teaspoon, $^1/_2$ teaspoon, $^1/_4$ teaspoon.

| Cup | | Spoon | |
|---|---|---|---|
| $^1/_4$ cup | = 60ml | $^1/_4$ teaspoon | = 1.25ml |
| $^1/_3$ cup | = 80ml | $^1/_2$ teaspoon | = 2.5ml |
| $^1/_2$ cup | = 125ml | 1 teaspoon | = 5ml |
| 1 cup | = 250ml | 1 tablespoon | = 20ml |

## Liquids

| Imperial | Metric | Metric |
|---|---|---|
| 1fl oz | - | 30 ml |
| 2fl oz | $^1/_4$ cup | 60ml |
| 3fl oz | - | 100ml |
| 4fl oz | $^1/_2$ cup | 125ml |
| 5fl oz | - | 150ml |
| 6fl oz | $^3/_4$ cup | 200ml |
| 8fl oz | 1 cup | 250ml |
| 10fl oz | $1^1/_4$ cups | 300ml |
| 12fl oz | $1^1/_2$ cups | 375ml |
| 14 fl oz | $1^3/_4$ cups | 425ml |
| 15fl oz | - | 475ml |
| 16fl oz | 2 cups | 500ml |
| 20fl oz (1 pint) | $2^1/_2$ cups | 600ml |

## Mass (weight)

(Approximate conversion for cookery purposes)

| Imperial | Metric | Imperial | Metric | |
|---|---|---|---|---|
| $^1/_2$ oz | 15g | 10oz | 315g | |
| 1oz | 30g | 11oz | 345g | |
| 2oz | 60g | 12oz ($^3/_4$lb) | 375g | |
| 3oz | 90g | 13oz | 410g | |
| 4oz ($^1/_4$lb) | 125g | 14oz | 440g | |
| 5oz | 155g | 15oz | 470g | |
| 6oz | 185g | 16oz (1lb) | 500g | (0.5kg) |
| 7oz | 220g | 24oz ($1^1/_2$lb) | 750g | |
| 8oz ($^1/_2$lb) | 250g | 32oz (2lb) | 1000g | (1kg) |
| 9oz | 280g | 3lb | 1500g | (1.5kg) |

## Oven temperatures

| Oven | Fahrenheit | Celsius |
|---|---|---|
| Very slow | 250° | 120° |
| Slow | 275–300° | 140–150° |
| Moderately slow | 325° | 160° |
| Moderate | 350° | 180° |
| Moderately hot | 375° | 190° |
| Hot | 400–450° | 200–230° |
| Very hot | 475–500° | 240–250° |

Note: For fan ovens set approximately 20° Celsius below
the stated temperature.

# index